DRAWINGS AND STORY BOARD:
MAURILIO TAVORMINA

EDITORIAL PROJECT AND PATENT:
FEDERICO SCHNEIDER

TEXTS:
MAURILIO TAVORMINA
AND
FEDERICO SCHNEIDER

COVER GRAPHICS:
DOPPIAVU
PHOTOS AND SCANNING:
SPAZIO VISIVO
TRANSLATION:
STEPHEN PAUL SCHNEIDER
REVIEW:
ROBERTO SCHNEIDER

BIBLIOGRAPHY
R. A. STACCIOLI, ROMA ANTICA, VISION 2000
F. COARELLI, GUIDA ARCHEOLOGICA DI ROMA, MONDADORI 1974
J. CARCOPINO, LA VITA QUOTIDIANA A ROMA, LATERZA 1987
C. NEUMEISTER, ROMA ANTICA. GUIDA LETTERARIA DELLA CITTÀ, SALERNO ED. 1993
F. DUPONT, LA VITA QUOTIDIANA NELLA ROMA REPUBBLICANA, LATERZA 2000
AA. VV., IL COLOSSEO, ELECTA 1999
AA. VV., ROME RESSUSCITÉE, PLON 1963
F. MEIJER, UN GIORNO AL COLOSSEO, LATERZA 2004
A. ANGELA, UNA GIORNATA NELL'ANTICA ROMA, RAI MONDADORI 2007

RECONSTRUCTIONS:
FOR VISION S.R.L.
TIZIANA D'ESTE

A SERIES BY VISION S.R.L.

PAST & PRESENT

VISION S.R.L.
VIA LIVORNO, 20 00162 ROME, ITALY
TEL/FAX: +39 06 44292688 E-MAIL: INFO@VISIONPUBL.COM

ISBN 978-88-8162-255-9

PRINTED IN ITALY BY TIPOLITOGRAFICA CS

SPECIAL ACKNOWLEDGMENTS
TOMMASO E GIACOMO MATTIUZZI,
RAFFAELLA SCHNEIDER, FIAMMA AJELLO
ALESSANDRA BONACCI, CINZIA VISMARA,
CHIARA MORSELLI, UGO FUSCO, DOMINGA PON
IRENE FUSCO, ADELE FERRAZZOLI,
GIUSEPPINA VENTURA

753 BC

FOUNDATION OF ROME

96-193 AD
DYNASTY OF THE ANTONINES

YOU MUST HELP TRAJAN BUILD HIS FORUM, WAIT FOR 1 TURN

69-96 AD
FLAVIAN DYNASTY

THEY BUILT THE COLOSSEUM, MOVE BACK 2 SQUARES

14-68 AD
JULIO-CLAUDIAN DYNASTY

753-510 BC
THE SEVEN KINGS OF ROME

MOVE AHEAD 7 SQUARES

SPQR

306-337 AD
CONSTANTINE

RE-ROLL THE DICE

193-235 AD
SEVERAN DYNASTY

SPQR

27 BC
OCTAVIAN AUGUSTUS
FIRST ROMAN EMPEROR

THE EMPIRE BEGINS, MOVE AHEAD 1 SQUARE

509 BC
BEGINNING OF THE REPUBLICAN AGE

476 AD
FALL OF THE WESTERN ROMAN EMPIRE

44 BC
CAESAR'S ASSASSINATION

YOU'R PART OF THE CONSPIRACY; MOVE BACK TO MONARCHY!

SPQR

390 BC
THE GAULS SACK ROME

GO BACK TO START

SPQR

343-314 BC
SAMNITE WARS

YOU'R A PRISONER STOP FOR ONE TURN

264-146 BC
PUNIC WARS

YOU STOPPED HANNIBAL; MOVE AHEAD 1 SQUARE

SPQR

60 BC
POMPEUS, CAESAR AND CRASSUS TRIUMVIRATE

THEY MAKE YOU MOVE AHEAD 3 SQUARES

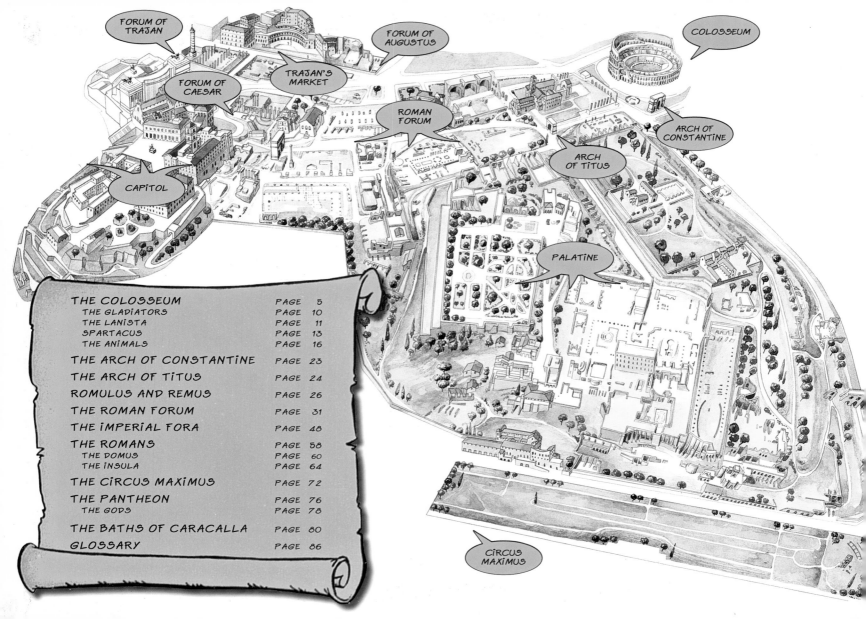

FORUM OF TRAJAN

FORUM OF AUGUSTUS

COLOSSEUM

FORUM OF CAESAR

TRAJAN'S MARKET

ROMAN FORUM

ARCH OF CONSTANTINE

ARCH OF TITUS

CAPITOL

PALATINE

CIRCUS MAXIMUS

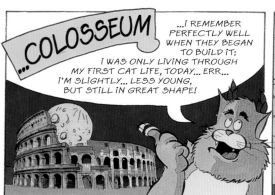

...COLOSSEUM

...I REMEMBER PERFECTLY WELL WHEN THEY BEGAN TO BUILD IT: I WAS ONLY LIVING THROUGH MY FIRST CAT LIFE, TODAY... ERR... I'M SLIGHTLY... LESS YOUNG, BUT STILL IN GREAT SHAPE!

WE WERE IN 70 AD AND VESPASIAN OF THE FLAVIUS FAMILY WAS THE EMPEROR OF ROME...

MY PREDECESSOR, EMPEROR NERO, HAS REIGNED AS A TYRANT AND AMONG THE ROMANS THERE STILL IS DISCONTENT! THE DOMUS AUREA, THE VILLA THAT HE HAD BUILT FOR HIMSELF, IS TRULY AN INSULT TO POVERTY!

WE MUST KEEP IN MIND THAT THE EMPEROR GOVERNS BUT ALSO CARES FOR THE PEOPLE OF ROME!

(AS HE THINKS) ERRR... GAMES... HMM... ERRR... COMBAT...

I GOT IT! I WILL HAVE A BUILDING CONSTRUCTED FOR GLADIATOR FIGHTS, WHERE CITIZENS OF ROME AND FROM ALL OVER THE EMPIRE MAY COME TO HAVE FUN!

I SHALL RETURN ROME TO THE ROMANS!

IT WAS CUSTOMARY DURING HOLIDAYS OR DURING FUNERALS OF ILLUSTRIOUS CITIZENS THAT GLADIATOR FIGHTS WOULD TAKE PLACE...

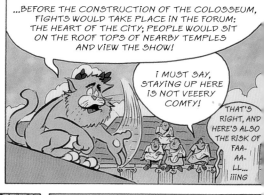

...BEFORE THE CONSTRUCTION OF THE COLOSSEUM, FIGHTS WOULD TAKE PLACE IN THE FORUM: THE HEART OF THE CITY; PEOPLE WOULD SIT ON THE ROOF TOPS OF NEARBY TEMPLES AND VIEW THE SHOW!

I MUST SAY, STAYING UP HERE IS NOT VEEERY COMFY!

THAT'S RIGHT, AND HERE'S ALSO THE RISK OF FAA-AA-LL... IIING

ONCE HE HAD SUMMONED THE ARCHITECTS, THE EMPEROR EXPLAINED HIS IDEA...

...EVERYTHING CLEAR? I WANT AN AMPHITHEATER, THE LARGEST AND MOST REGAL IN THE EMPIRE! I WILL CALL IT FLAVIAN AMPHITHEATER TO HONOR THE NAME OF MY FAMILY! NOW, LET'S GET STARTED!

HOW ABOUT BUILDING IT ON THE SAME SPOT OF THE ARTIFICIAL LAKE, AFTER DRAINING IT, OF THE...

...DOMUS AUREA: GREAT IDEA !! YET THE NAME " FLAVIAN AMPHITHEATER" IS NOT SO ORIGINAL!

BAH! I WOULD CALL IT... LET ME SEE... CO... COLOSSEUM! NOW THIS SOUNDS BETTER!

TRUE FACT IS THAT THE NAME OF COLOSSEUM WAS GIVEN ONLY IN THE MIDDLE AGES MAYBE DUE TO ITS SIZE OR TO ITS BEING CLOSE TO THIS COLOSSAL STATUE OF NERO!

WONDER IF I CAN TICKLE HIM?

HAVE SOME RESPECT YOU HAIRY CRUMB!

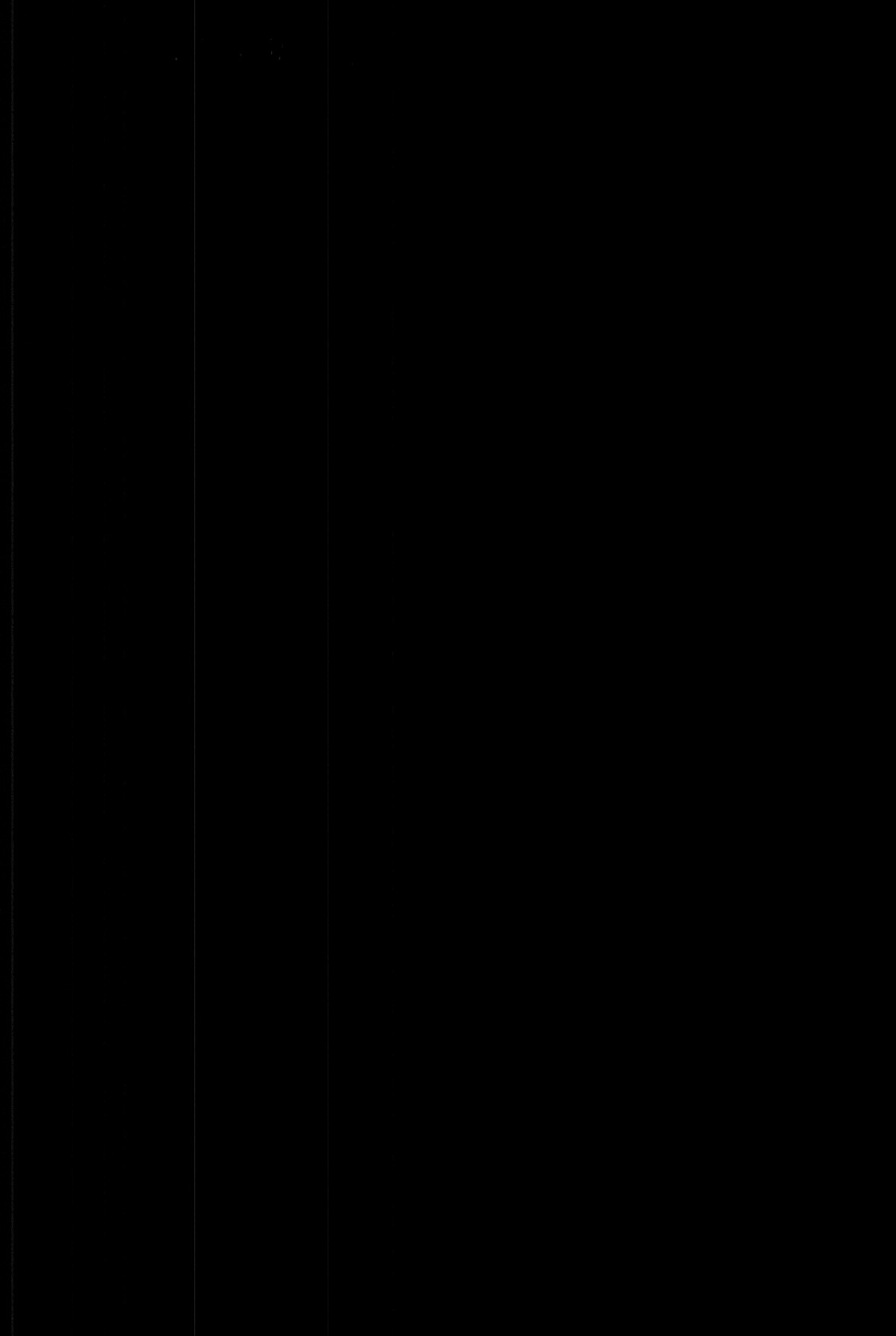

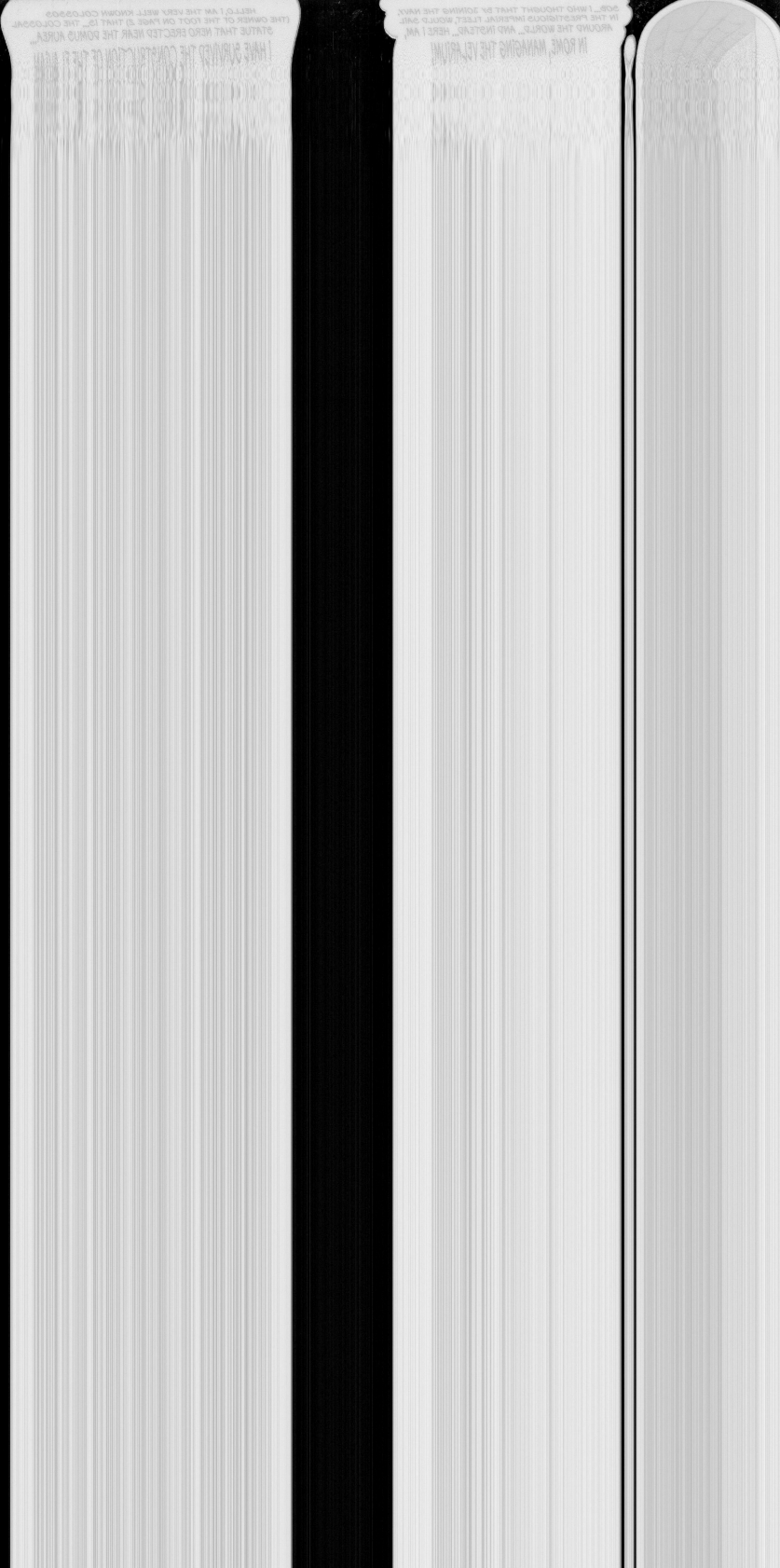

THE GLADIATORS

WHO WERE THESE GLADIATORS? HOW DID YA BECOME A GLADIATOR? HOW DID THEY LIVE? WHAT WOULD THEY MUNCH ON? YOU'LL FIND IT OUT IN THE NEXT CARTOON STRIPS...

AFTER EVERY CONQUEST, THE ROMAN ARMY MADE PRISONERS AND TURNED WHOEVER DID NOT ACKNOWLEDGE ROMAN SUPERIORITY INTO SLAVES... OFTEN SENTENCING THEM TO DEATH AS AN ATTRACTION FOR THE AUDIENCE IN THE ARENA... OR...

SHUCKS! I'VE BEEN CONDEMNED AD GLADIUM, THAT IS THEY WILL SPIT ME LIKE A CHICKEN!

LUCKY YOU! THEY SENTENCED ME AD BESTIAS (TO THE BEASTS), I'LL BE DEVOURED BY FEROCIOUS ANIMALS AND I DON'T EVEN TASTE GOOD!

ME INSTEAD CRUCIFIXIO, MEANING I WILL BE CRUCIFIED IN THE MIDDLE OF THE ARENA, AND I WILL HAVE TO WITNESS YOU TWO DYING!

WELL, IN THE WORST OF FATE I'VE HAD IT EASY: SENTENCED TO AD LUDUM GLADIATORIUM...

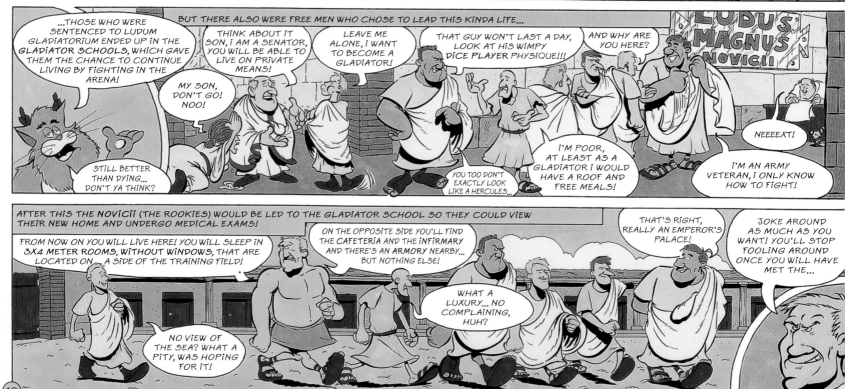

...THOSE WHO WERE SENTENCED TO LUDUM GLADIATORIUM ENDED UP IN THE GLADIATOR SCHOOLS, WHICH GAVE THEM THE CHANCE TO CONTINUE LIVING BY FIGHTING IN THE ARENA!

BUT THERE ALSO WERE FREE MEN WHO CHOSE TO LEAD THIS KINDA LIFE...

MY SON, DON'T GO! NOO!

STILL BETTER THAN DYING... DON'T YA THINK?

THINK ABOUT IT SON, I AM A SENATOR, YOU WILL BE ABLE TO LIVE ON PRIVATE MEANS!

LEAVE ME ALONE, I WANT TO BECOME A GLADIATOR!

THAT GUY WON'T LAST A DAY, LOOK AT HIS WIMPY DICE PLAYER PHYSIQUE!!!

YOU TOO DON'T EXACTLY LOOK LIKE A HERCULES...

I'M POOR, AT LEAST AS A GLADIATOR I WOULD HAVE A ROOF AND FREE MEALS!

AND WHY ARE YOU HERE?

NEEEEXT!

I'M AN ARMY VETERAN, I ONLY KNOW HOW TO FIGHT!

LUDUS MAGNUS NOVICII

AFTER THIS THE NOVICII (THE ROOKIES) WOULD BE LED TO THE GLADIATOR SCHOOL SO THEY COULD VIEW THEIR NEW HOME AND UNDERGO MEDICAL EXAMS!

FROM NOW ON YOU WILL LIVE HERE! YOU WILL SLEEP IN 3X4 METER ROOMS, WITHOUT WINDOWS, THAT ARE LOCATED ON ... A SIDE OF THE TRAINING FIELD!

NO VIEW OF THE SEA? WHAT A PITY, WAS HOPING FOR IT!

ON THE OPPOSITE SIDE YOU'LL FIND THE CAFETERIA AND THE INFIRMARY AND THERE'S AN ARMORY NEARBY... BUT NOTHING ELSE!

WHAT A LUXURY... NO COMPLAINING, HUH?

THAT'S RIGHT, REALLY AN EMPEROR'S PALACE!

JOKE AROUND AS MUCH AS YOU WANT! YOU'LL STOP FOOLING AROUND ONCE YOU WILL HAVE MET THE...

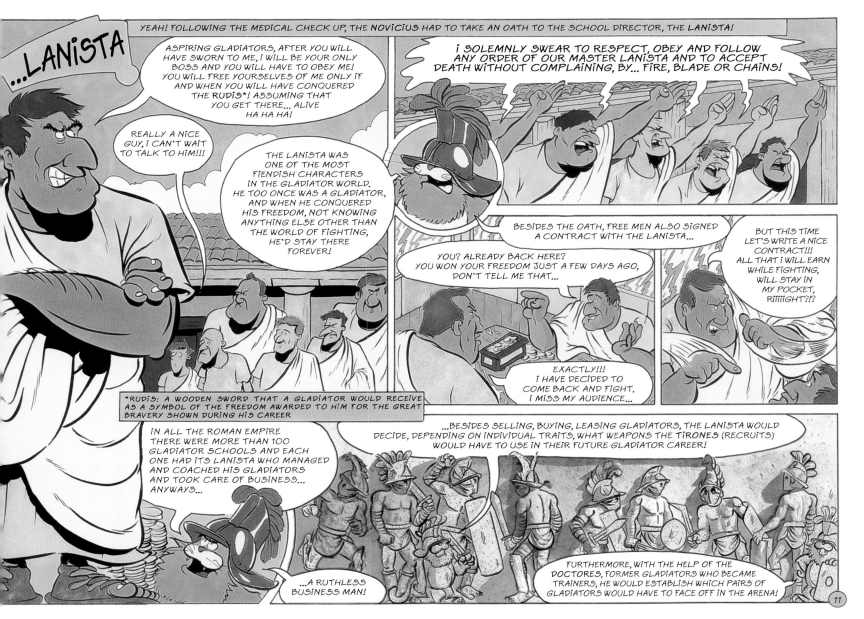

...LANISTA

ASPIRING GLADIATORS, AFTER YOU WILL HAVE SWORN TO ME, I WILL BE YOUR ONLY BOSS AND YOU WILL HAVE TO OBEY ME! YOU WILL FREE YOURSELVES OF ME ONLY IF AND WHEN YOU WILL HAVE CONQUERED THE RUDIS*! ASSUMING THAT YOU GET THERE... ALIVE HA HA HA!

REALLY A NICE GUY, I CAN'T WAIT TO TALK TO HIM!!!

THE LANISTA WAS ONE OF THE MOST FIENDISH CHARACTERS IN THE GLADIATOR WORLD. HE TOO ONCE WAS A GLADIATOR, AND WHEN HE CONQUERED HIS FREEDOM, NOT KNOWING ANYTHING ELSE OTHER THAN THE WORLD OF FIGHTING, HE'D STAY THERE FOREVER!

I SOLEMNLY SWEAR TO RESPECT, OBEY AND FOLLOW ANY ORDER OF OUR MASTER LANISTA AND TO ACCEPT DEATH WITHOUT COMPLAINING, BY... FIRE, BLADE OR CHAINS!

BESIDES THE OATH, FREE MEN ALSO SIGNED A CONTRACT WITH THE LANISTA...

YOU? ALREADY BACK HERE? YOU WON YOUR FREEDOM JUST A FEW DAYS AGO, DON'T TELL ME THAT...

EXACTLY!!! I HAVE DECIDED TO COME BACK AND FIGHT. I MISS MY AUDIENCE...

BUT THIS TIME LET'S WRITE A NICE CONTRACT!!! ALL THAT I WILL EARN WHILE FIGHTING, WILL STAY IN MY POCKET, RIIIIIGHT?!?

*RUDIS: A WOODEN SWORD THAT A GLADIATOR WOULD RECEIVE AS A SYMBOL OF THE FREEDOM AWARDED TO HIM FOR THE GREAT BRAVERY SHOWN DURING HIS CAREER

IN ALL THE ROMAN EMPIRE THERE WERE MORE THAN 100 GLADIATOR SCHOOLS AND EACH ONE HAD ITS LANISTA WHO MANAGED AND COACHED HIS GLADIATORS AND TOOK CARE OF BUSINESS... ANYWAYS...

...A RUTHLESS BUSINESS MAN!

...BESIDES SELLING, BUYING, LEASING GLADIATORS, THE LANISTA WOULD DECIDE, DEPENDING ON INDIVIDUAL TRAITS, WHAT WEAPONS THE TIRONES (RECRUITS) WOULD HAVE TO USE IN THEIR FUTURE GLADIATOR CAREER!

FURTHERMORE, WITH THE HELP OF THE DOCTORES, FORMER GLADIATORS WHO BECAME TRAINERS, HE WOULD ESTABLISH WHICH PAIRS OF GLADIATORS WOULD HAVE TO FACE OFF IN THE ARENA!

HUFF... PANT... THE INITIAL TRAINING... PANT OF THE TIRONES CONSISTED OF HITTING A SEVEN FOOT HIGH POLE, THE PALUS, WITH WOODEN WEAPONS!

HEY BALDY, YOU LOOK LIKE SOMEONE IN THE KNOW, CAN YOU TELL ME HOW THE TRAINING WORKS OUT?

KID, SHOW SOME RESPECT: I AM A VETERANUS, THAT IS I HAVE ALREADY FOUGHT AND WON IN THE ARENA, I'LL SHOW YOU...

...D'YOU SEE THAT GUY WHO'S TRAINING BY THE PALUS? HE IS THE BEST OF YOU ROOKIES AND HE HAS DESERVED THE AWARD OF PRIMUS PALUS (THE TOP LEVEL), THEN IN THE RANKING COME THE SECUNDUS PALUS...

...THE TERTIUS PALUS AND SO FORTH UNTIL THE LAST, THE WORST, KNOWN AS SPECTATUS, WHO IS...

...THE SON OF THE SENATOR? BUT HE RAN OFF THIS MORNING!

A'RIGHT... THEN KID THAT MAKES YOU THE SPECTATUS!

AT THE END OF TRAINING THE WEAPONS WOULD BE PUT BACK...

DARN...THIS TRAINING'S TIRING, I'M GETTING HUNGRY!!!

THE TRAINING IS OVER HURRY UP! I HAVE TO CLOSE THE ARMORY!

JUDGING FROM THE SMELL THERE'S PROBABLY THE SAME OLD BARLEY SOUP!

...IN THE ARMORY

YOU SURE ABOUT THE SOUP? THE PRIMUS PALUS HAD TOLD ME THERE WOULD BE MEAT TODAY...

NO, IT'S ONLY FOR HIM! HE'S THE BEST OF THE BARRACKS AND THE LANISTA TREATS HIM WELL! BUT I DON'T CARE, TONIGHT...

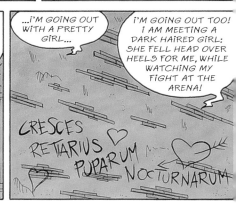

...I'M GOING OUT WITH A PRETTY GIRL...

I'M GOING OUT TOO! I AM MEETING A DARK HAIRED GIRL: SHE FELL HEAD OVER HEELS FOR ME, WHILE WATCHING MY FIGHT AT THE ARENA!

CRESCES RETIARIUS ♡ PUPARUM ♡ NOCTURNARUM

MUSCULAR AND FULL OF COURAGE, THE GLADIATORS WOULD FASCINATE YOUNG LADIES, WHO WOULD FILL THE WALLS OF THE GLADIATOR SCHOOLS WITH LOVE GRAFFITI!

...THEN WHEN THE CRUSH IS OVER YOU DON'T SEE THEM ANYMORE AND YOU DON'T HEAR FROM THEM EITHER, OH WELL!

THAT'S RIGHT! COME ON, LET'S GO CHEER OURSELVES UP IN THE KITCHEN!

SO COOK, WHAT GOOD STUFF HAVE YOU PREPARED... TODAY?

FLAMINGO TONGUES?

FRIED MICE?

BARLEY AND BEAN SOUP THAT WILL FATTEN YOU UP AND THEREFORE HELP PROTECT YOU FROM WOUNDS! YOUR HEALTH DEPENDS ON ME, SO YOU SHOULD QUIT CLOWNING AROUND IN THE KITCHEN...

RARELY HAVE SUCH PROPHETIC WORDS COME FROM A COOK! CAN YOU BELIEVE THAT JUST FROM THE KITCHEN OF A GLADIATOR SCHOOL, THE ONE IN CAPUA, A REBELLION BROKE OUT THAT SUBDUED ROME!!! THE LEADER OF THE REBELLION WAS A CERTAIN...

SPARTACUS
AND THE REBELS OF
CAPUA

...IN 73 BC SPARTACUS, A GLADIATOR ORIGINALLY FROM THRACE (TODAY BETWEEN GREECE AND BULGARIA) ORGANIZED A REBELLION ALONG WITH OTHER MATES OF HIS IN THE GLADIATOR SCHOOL IN CAPUA...

GLADIATORS, I WANT TO SEE YOU AT FULL STRENGTH!!!

HERE IS SPARTACUS! HE WAS BORN IN A FAMILY OF SHEPHERDS LIVING IN RAGS AND WAS FORCED TO ENLIST OUT OF NEED WITH THE ROMAN ARMY: HE DESERTED, WAS CAUGHT AND ENSLAVED, THEN BECAME A GLADIATOR...

LAZYBONES! COME ON, GET MOVING!

I'M FED UP! I MUST APPLY THE ESCAPE PLAN THAT I HAVE BEEN PREPARING WITH MY MATES ENOMAUS AND CRISSUS. TODAY OR NEVER AGAIN!

ENOUGH OF THIS! THE LANISTA IS MASSACRING US!

THEREFORE THAT NIGHT THEY ALL MET IN THE KITCHENS...

SPARTACUS WE ARE ALL WITH YOU!!! BUT HOW WILL WE MANAGE? WE ONLY HAVE KITCHEN KNIVES!

CUBRICUS, TRUST ME! THEY ARE GOOD KNIVES...

NAAH... I'M UNABLE EVEN TO USE THEM TO CUT MEAT

...WE ARE GLADIATORS, WE SHALL MANAGE TO FIGHT EVEN WITH THESE!

THE REBELS MANAGED TO FLEE FROM THE TRAINING SCHOOL, TOOK POSSESSION OF THE WEAPONS OF A UNIT SENT TO STOP THEM AND BARRICADED THEMSELVES ON MOUNT VESUVIUS. THE ROMANS WERE...

...CERTAIN OF HAVING TRAPPED THEM!

BY NOW THEY HAVE BEEN SURROUNDED FOR SEVERAL DAYS!

RETREAT INSIDE VESUVIUS... WHAT MADNESS! THEY WILL NEVER MAKE IT OUT ALIVE!

INSTEAD, PASSING THROUGH THE FISSURES IN THE CRATER...

COME ON GUYS! WE HAVE CAUGHT THEM BY SURPRISE!

THE REVOLT GREW, AND OTHER SLAVES JOINED SPARTACUS. FOR THREE YEARS THE REBELS MANAGED TO EVADE DETECTION, UNTIL THE ROMANS, UNDERSTANDING THEY WERE DEALING WITH VERY WELL TRAINED MEN LONGING FOR FREEDOM, DECIDED TO FACE THEM WITH A REAL AND PROPER ARMY!

...WE ARE SURROUNDED!!! BUT WE WILL DIE AS FREE MEN!

ANYHOW, SPARTACUS, WE BEGAN WITH KITCHEN KNIVES... WHAT ELSE WOULD YOU EXPECT?

HENCE THIS IS WHY THE ROMANS INCREASED THEIR CONTROL OF GLADIATOR SCHOOLS, AND ESPECIALLY IN THE KITCHENS!

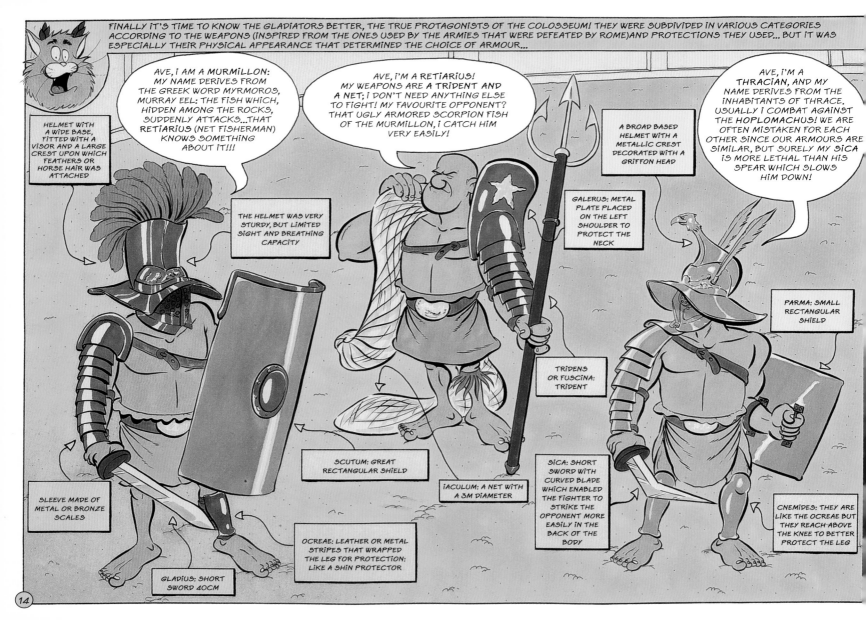

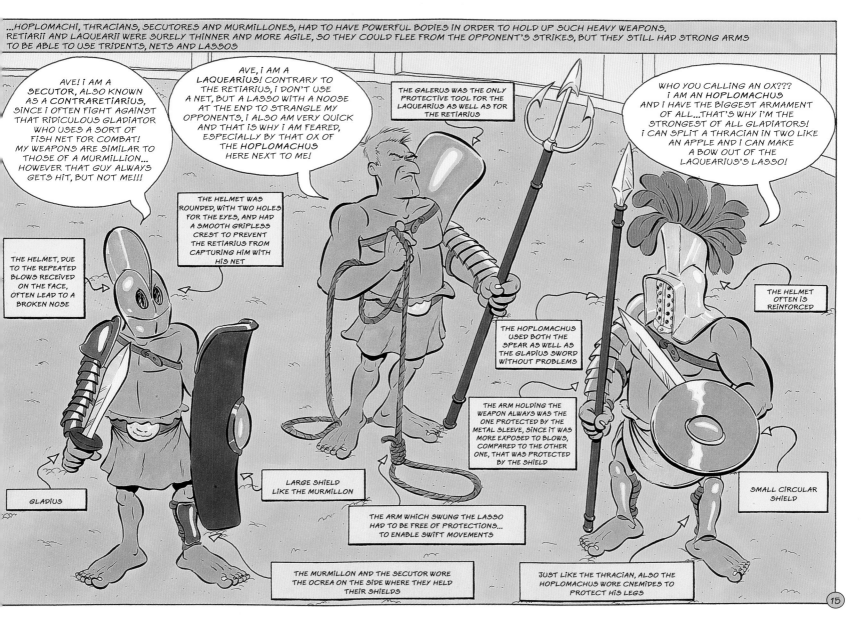

THE PROTAGONISTS OF THESE SHOWS WERE THE VENATORES (HUNTERS) WHO EXHIBITED THEIR HUNTING SKILLS AGAINST HARMLESS ANIMALS (OSTRICHES, ANTILOPES ETC.) AND THE BESTIARII WHO INSTEAD FOUGHT AGAINST SAVAGE ANIMALS OFTEN... BAREHANDED!

DURING THESE SHOWS THE ARENA WAS...

...DECORATED AS A FOREST!

ANIMALS WEREN'T ONLY USED FOR VIOLENT SHOWS, BUT ALSO FOR CIRCUS EXHIBITIONS AND GAMES IN WHICH THEY DISPLAYED THEIR INTELLIGENCE!

HERE'S YOUR GAMES DIRECTOR, MICAEL BONADIES, SPEAKING TO ALL YOU HAPPY FOLKS! TODAY, AS AN INTELLIGENCE TEST WE WILL WITNESS A CHALLENGE OF "LEAVE THE CAGE" BETWEEN NONE OTHER THAN...

BETTER NOT DISTRACT ME, MAKING ME LAUGH... I WANT TO LOOK MY BEST!

HA HA...OF COURSE...HA HA... I'LL DO IT, BUT YOU'RE ONE STEP AHEAD: YOU'VE GOT AN ELEPHANT'S MEMORY... HA, HA, HA!

AN ELEPHANT AND A LAUGHING HYENA: ARE YOU READY??

PUBLIC EXECUTIONS WERE PROGRAMMED IN THE MIDDLE OF THE ARENA DURING LUNCH TIME ; THIS IS STUFF I'D RATHER NOT TELL YOU ABOUT... BUT ONCE...

SOB... POOR ME! SENTENCED TO DEATH IN THE COLOSSEUM ONLY FOR HAVING FLED FROM MY MASTER WHO MISTREATED ME! NOW I WILL BE DEVOURED BY A WILD ANIMAL... HERE COMES A LION!

INCREDIBLE, THIS IS THE SAME LION THAT I CAME ACROSS WHEN I WAS ESCAPING AND HELPED BY PULLING OUT A THORN STUCK IN HIS PAW! HE HAS RECOGNIZED ME AND IS NOT ATTACKING!

THE GAME ORGANIZER WAS FURIOUS, SO HE THEN INTRODUCED A LEOPARD INTO THE ARENA TO HAVE BOTH OF THEM MAULED, BUT...

WHO WOULD HAVE THOUGHT IT: MY FATE SAVED ME!

...IN THE END BOTH THE LION AND THE SLAVE ANDROCLUS OBTAINED THEIR FREEDOM!

19

IN THE AFTERNOON THE MAIN EVENT OF THE DAY TOOK PLACE: GLADIATOR FIGHTS! IT WAS ANNOUNCED BY A CEREMONIAL PROCESSION...

TOGA-WEARING LICTORS (ROMAN CIVIL SERVANTS) CARRIED THE FASCES, SYMBOL OF POWER

TRUMPET PLAYERS

BLACKSMITHS CARRIED ON A STRETCHER FORGING WEAPONS, TO GUARANTEE THAT THE MATCH WOULD TAKE PLACE WITHOUT TRICKS

TABLE WITH THE PROGRAM OF THE FIGHTS

OLIVE BRANCH, AWARD FOR THE VICTOR

EVENT ORGANIZER

SERVANTS WHO SHOW THE GLADIATORS' WEAPONS

...AND NOW... ARRIVING FROM EVERY CORNER OF THE EMPIRE, TO ENTERTAIN AND EXCITE THE PEOPLE OF ROME, HERE FOR YOU...THE GLADIATOOOORS!!!

...PSSST

HUH!?

...I FEEL LIKE FIGHTING IN THE ARENA, FIND 4 OR 5 GUYS IN BAD SHAPE AND ARM THEM WITH LITTLE SWORDS AND MINIATURE SHIELDS!

THEN PREPARE THE HERCULES COSTUME AND ANNOUNCE TO THE PUBLIC THAT TODAY EMPEROR COMMODUS HIMSELF WILL BE FIGHTING!!!

OH YEAH!... EVEN THIS HAPPENED: SOME EMPERORS WERE ATTRACTED BY THE GLAMOUR OF THE ARENA, SO TO SHOW OFF THEIR PROWESS THEY FOUGHT LIKE GLADIATORS! AMONG THEM THE MOST FAMOUS WAS COMMODUS, WHO DRESSED UP AS HERCULES!

OBVIOUSLY ONE WAY OR ANOTHER THE EMPEROR ALWAYS WON!

PEOPLE OF ROME, I, COMMODUS, LIKE HERCULES DURING IS HEROIC ADVENTURES, SHALL FACE THESE VALIANT FIGHTERS BY MYSELF!

THIS GUY IS NUTS!!!

??

WELL!

VALIANT FIGHTERS? WITH THESE WEAPONS???

AND THE SPECTATORS, WHETHER THEY WANTED IT OR NOT...

GO, GO COMMODUS!

COME ON!

KILL'EM!

WHAT A DISGRACE! EVEN I COULD BEAT THOSE LOSERS!

YEAH, BUT HE'S THE EMPEROR...

YEAH!

THEREFORE COMMODUS ALWAYS WON AND THE SPECTATORS WERE FORCED TO CHEER HIM AS A WORTHY FIGHTER... BUT WHEN THE REAL GLADIATORS ENTERED...

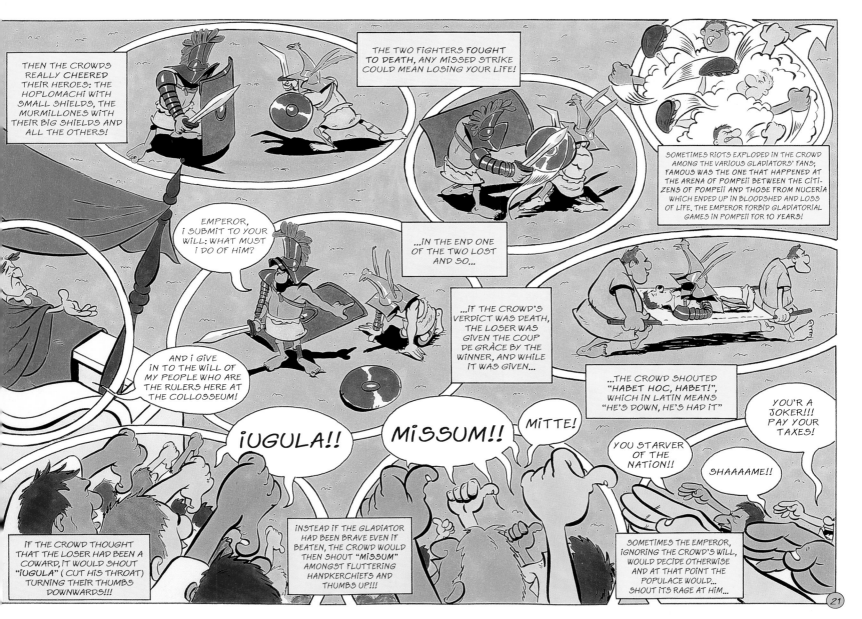

THE COLOSSEUM'S MAJESTY SURE GIVES PROOF OF ROME'S MIGHT BUT WHAT REALLY MADE IT GREAT WERE ALL THE BATTLES WON AND THE CONQUESTS MADE, CELEBRATED AND MADE ETERNAL BY THE TRIUMPHAL ARCHES! ...

THE ARCH OF CONSTANTINE

WE'RE IN YEAR 312 AD AND ROME WILL SHORTLY NO LONGER BE THE EMPIRE'S CAPITAL. THE EMPEROR HAS DECIDED TO MOVE HIS RESIDENCE TO BYZANTIUM (NOW ISTANBUL, TURKEY), AND NOTWITHSTANDING THIS, THE SENATE IS STILL DISCUSSING ON THE POSSIBLE CONSTRUCTION OF...

...A TRIUMPHAL ARCH!! WE'VE GOT TO CELEBRATE CONSTANTINE'S VICTORY OVER MAXENTIUS!

GREAT IDEA! BUT ALL OF OUR BEST SCULPTORS AND STONE CUTTERS HAVE ALREADY MOVED TO BYZANTIUM!

AT LEAST THERE THEY CAN WORK!

IT'S REALLY A BIG PROBLEM... HOW CAN WE DECORATE THE ARCH WITH RELIEFS AND SCULPTURES?

I'VE GOT AN IDEA!!!

WE'LL TAKE DECORATIONS AND SCULPTURES FROM SOME OF THE OLD MONUMENTS ALSO SAVING A PENNY ON THE WAY... HE, HE!!!

WONDERFUL!! MORE SO SINCE SOME OF THE MONUMENTS ARE ALREADY IN RUINS! SO THE STATUES AND RELIEFS THAT MADE FAMOUS THE FEATS OF EMPERORS LIKE MARCUS AURELIUS, TRAJAN AND HADRIAN WILL NOW CELEBRATE THE GLORY OF EMPEROR CONSTANTINE!

3 METER HIGH PANELS RECYCLED FROM THE MONUMENT DEDICATED TO MARCUS AURELIUS: THEY DESCRIBE THIS EMPEROR'S MAIN BATTLES!

INSCRIPTION DEDICATED TO CONSTANTINE: "TO EMPEROR CAESAR FLAVIUS CONSTANTINE MAXIMUS, DEVOUT AND FORTUNATE, AUGUST, SINCE THROUGH DIVINE INSPIRATION AND GREAT WISDOM WITH HIS ARMY HE AVENGED WITH NOBLE ARMS AT THE SAME TIME THE STATE AGAINST A TYRANT AND AGAINST ALL HIS FACTIONS, THE SENATE AND THE ROMAN PEOPLE HAVE DEDICATED THIS OUTSTANDING TRIUMPHAL ARCH"

8 STATUES (4 ON EACH SIDE) SHOWING DACIAN PRISONERS IN CHAINS, RECYCLED FROM EMPEROR TRAJAN'S FORUM (SEE PAGE 53)

ROUND DECORATONS SHOWING MYTHOLOGICAL SCENES OF HUNTS AND SACRIFICES ALSO RECYCLED FROM A PREVIOUS MONUMENT DEDICATED TO HADRIAN

FINALLY SOME ORIGINAL RELIEFS! THEY SHOW EPISODES FROM THE WAR BETWEEN CONSTANTINE AND MAXENTIUS

THESE RELIEFS DEPICT VICTORIES (REPRESENTED AS DIVINITIES IN HUMAN FORMS) AND BARBARIAN PRISONERS

THREE ARCHWAY STRUCTURE

HERE WE WALK INTO THE HEART OF ANCIENT ROME: THE ROMAN FORUM! TO GET THERE WE'VE GOT TO STROLL ALONG THE UPPER VIA SACRA, WHICH FROM THE COLOSSEUM LEADS ALL THE WAY TO THE CAPITOL HILL! WHO KNOWS HOW MANY NOBLE FEET TROD ON THESE SAME STONE SLABS!

AND AS AN IMPOSING ENTRY TO THE FORUM, WE FIND...

...THE ARCH OF TITUS

IT WAS ERECTED AROUND 81 AD BY EMPEROR DOMITIAN IN HONOUR OF HIS BROTHER TITUS WHO HAD ENDED THE WAR IN JUDEA WITH THE SACK OF...

...JERUSALEM! OUR POOR JERUSALEM!!! THE ROMANS EVEN DESTROYED OUR TEMPLE LEAVING ONLY THIS WALL AGAINST WHICH WE CAN STILL PRAY AND WAIL!

EVEN SADDER IS THE CAPTURE AND DEPORTATION OF 10.000 OF OUR FELLOW JEWS AND THE REST HAD TO FLEE!

I EVEN HEARD THE RUMOR THAT OUR BROTHERS WHO WERE MADE SLAVES, HAVE BEEN FORCED TO WORK ON THE CONSTRUCTION OF THE COLOSSEUM!!

YEAH, THAT'S WHAT'S BEING SAID... BUT THE BIGGEST ABOMINATION OF ALL IS THAT TITUS'S BROTHER, EMPEROR DOMITIAN WHO IS NOW IN POWER...

INSCRIPTION DEDICATED TO EMPEROR TITUS: "THE SENATE AND PEOPLE OF ROME TO DIVINE TITUS, SON OF THE DIVINE VESPASIANUS, VESPASIANUS AUGUSTUS"

PANEL SHOWING ANOTHER SCENE FROM THE TRIUMPHAL PROCESSION: TITUS RIDES A QUADRIGA (4 HORSE-DRAWN CHARIOT) SURROUNDED BY MYTHOLOGICAL FIGURES CELEBRATING HIS TRIUMPH

PANEL FEATURING TITUS'S TRIUMPHAL PARADE AFTER HIS CAMPAIGN IN JUDEA, THE DETAILS OF THE DECORATION INCLUDE SOLDIERS TRANSPORTING BOOTY FROM THE TEMPLE OF JERUSALEM: THE SILVER TRUMPETS, THE SEVEN-BRANCHED CANDELABRUM, THE MENORAH, IN ONE OF ITS MOST ANCIENT REPRESENTATIONS

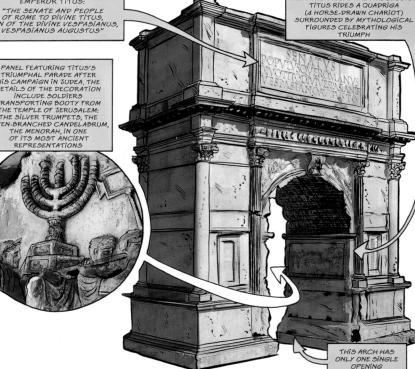

...DECIDED TO BUILD INSIDE THE ROMAN FORUM A TRIUMPHAL ARCH TO CELEBRATE HIS FATHER'S AND HIS BROTHER'S CONQUESTS IN OUR LAND! NO JEW, THROUGHOUT CENTURIES MUST EVER PASS UNDERNEATH THAT VILE ARCH!

THIS ARCH HAS ONLY ONE SINGLE OPENING

ROMULUS AND REMUS

THE SONS OF THE SHE-WOLF

ONCE UPON A TIME WHEN ROME DID NOT YET EXIST, LATIUM WAS DOMINATED BY THE CITY OF ALBA, RULED BY THE TREACHEROUS KING AMULIUS WHO HAD OUSTED FROM POWER HIS GOOD BROTHER NUMITOR...

IT'S A KID'S GAME TO STEAL SHEEP FROM NUMITOR'S FIELDS!

...STEALING FROM HIM IS LIKE SCORNING HIS SINISTER BROTHER AMULIUS! TOO BAD ROMULUS DOESN'T FOLLOW ME IN THESE RAIDS; HE'S TOO MUCH OF A GOOD GUY!

DARN IT, HERE ARE KING AMULIUS'S SHEPHERDS!

YOU'VE STOPPED BEING A SMART ALECK! NOW WE'RE REALLY GOING TO TEACH YOU A LESSON!

FROM BEHIND A TREE ROMULUS WAS LOOKING ON...

ROMULUS, STOP STARING AT ME... TAKE THE SHEEP AND RUN FOR IT!

...AND GO HOME AND TELL WHAT'S HAPPENED...

ROMULUS WHERE IS YOUR BROTHER?

WHILE HE WAS STEALING NUMITOR'S SHEEP, HE WAS CAPTURED BY THE KING'S SHEPHERDS!! I MUST GO AND HELP HIM!

FAUSTULUS, MAYBE IT'S TIME YOU TELL HIM EVERYTHING!

YOU'RE RIGHT LARENTIA, THE TIME HAS COME!

YOU SEE ROMULUS, WE FOUND YOU BOTH AS INFANTS NEAR A GROTTO, NOT FAR FROM THE TIBER, BEING TAKEN CARE OF BY A SHE-WOLF!

IN THE WOLF'S DEN THERE WAS ALSO A SOGGY BASKET, WHICH MEANS THAT THE SHE-WOLF HAD DRAGGED YOU OUT OF THE RIVER

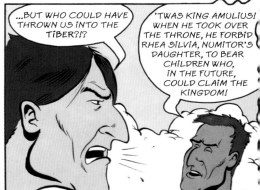

...BUT WHO COULD HAVE THROWN US INTO THE TIBER?!?

'TWAS KING AMULIUS! WHEN HE TOOK OVER THE THRONE, HE FORBID RHEA SILVIA, NUMITOR'S DAUGHTER, TO BEAR CHILDREN WHO, IN THE FUTURE, COULD CLAIM THE KINGDOM!

BUT RHEA SILVIA, BORE CHILDREN... NONETHELESS FROM THE GOD MARS AND THEY WERE TWINS: YOU TWO!

FINE! SO NOW I HAVE REASON TO KILL AMULIUS

...ROMULUS THEN WENT TO SEEK FOR HIS BROTHER; NUMITOR RECOGNISING HIM AS HIS GRANDSON, FREED REMUS AND BOTH ONCE REUNITED, KILLED AMULIUS...

REMUS, WHAT D'YOU THINK ABOUT FOUNDING OUR OWN CITY, RIGHT ON THE SPOT WHERE THE SHE-WOLF SAVED US!

GREAT IDEA! BUT WHO WILL BE THE RULER OF US TWO? TWO LEADERS WOULD BE TOO MANY!

TO DECIDE, THEY FOLLOWED GRANPA NUMITOR'S ADVICE, AND THEY ENTRUSTED THEMSELVES TO AN OLD CUSTOM, THE AUSPICIES: HE WHO SEES MORE BIRDS, WINS!!

12!!! SORRY REMUS, BUT I'LL BE THE RULER!

OK! ROMULUS, BUT WHAT A SILLY WAY TO BET ON A KINGDOM!

..SO ROMULUS, DREW THE LIMITS TO HIS CITY WITH A PLOUGH'S FURROW AND THEN...

...WE'VE BUILT WALLS AND EVEN IF THE'RE MODEST THEY MUST BE DEFENDED... WITH ALL YE MIGHT AND MEANS!!!

... BUT REMUS, MAYBE AS A JOKE MAYBE AS A CHALLENGE...

ROMULUS SURELY HAD REALLY CHEEKY LUCK!

NOW I'LL JUMP OVER HIS LITTLE WALL AND MAKE FUN OF HIM!

HI'YA MEN! WHERE IS ROMULUS? I MUST CONGRATULATE HIM FOR THE VERY HIGH WALL! HO, HO HO!

HEY! BUT WHAT ARE YOU DOING WITH THOSE SPEARS?! ROMUUUULUSSS...

THAT'S HOW REMUS WAS KILLED BY HIS BROTHER'S TOO OBEDIENT MEN. SO ROMULUS FOUNDED HIS CITY, IT WAS APRIL 21ST 753 BC THE DATE THAT CELEBRATES ROME'S FOUNDATION!

IT'S ONE OF THE MANY TALES; THE'RE LEGENDS TOLD ONLY TO EMBELLISH ROME'S HISTORY...

...OR PERHAPS THEY ARE SYMBOLS: IN THIS CASE REMUS MEANS IGNORANCE THAT IS AN OBSTACLE TO THE BIRTH...

...OF CIVILIZATION REPRESENTED BY ROMULUS! YOU'R ONLY A SUCKER... AND THEN... THE STORY OF THE SHE-WOLF... HUH?

SINCE YOU'R SPEAKING LIKE A SO-CALLED PHILOSOPHER, YOU WILL AT LEAST ADMIT THAT IN EVERY LEGEND THERE'S ALWAYS...

...SOME HIDDEN TRUTH, INDEED IT HAS BEEN PROVEN THAT HERE ON THE PALATINE HILL, THE FIRST NUCLEUS WAS BORN OF WHAT TODAY HAS BECOME A GREAT EMPIRE!

HEY! YOU TWO LAZY BONES! QUIT YOUR CHATTING AND GET ON RESTORING ROMULUS'S HUT!

THESE LOUSY SOGGY PIECES OF WOOD COULD NOT HAVE BEEN FIT EVEN FOR A STABLE!

IN ANY CASE, ROME WAS BORN ON THE PALATINE AND SO THIS HUT IS NOW VERY IMPORTANT!

THAT'S WHY, SINCE THE TIMES OF AUGUSTUS, ALL EMPERORS COME HERE ON THE PALATINE TO BUILD THEIR PALACES, THE WAY ROMULUS DID IN THE BEGINNING!

BY THE WAY JUST THINK ABOUT IT: THE WORD "PALACE" COMES FROM "PALATIUM" THE LATIN NAME OF THE... PALATINE HILL!

THIS IS A SACRED PLACE FOR US ROMANS! HERE THE SON OF MARS STARTED THE HISTORY OF ROME!

TSK TSK... ROMULUS MIGHT HAVE BEEN THE SON OF MARS THE GOD, BUT HE GREW UP STEALING SHEEP AND... SO WE DESCEND FROM ROBBERS AND RUNAWAYS!

YOU TRAITOR, WHAT'YOU'R SAYING?!?! 'LL TAKE YOU TO JAIL FOR THIS!!

BUT LISTEN TO HIM!?! HE'S MAKING BELIEVE HE DOESN'T KNOW IT... IT'S THE LEGEND ITSELF THAT SAY'S SO!!

....

WELL, ACTUALLY HE'S NOT ALL THAT WRONG!

ROME HAD JUST BEEN FOUNDED AND ROMULUS WAS WORRIED...

SURE THING IF I DON'T HAVE ENOUGH SOLDIERS TO DEFEND ROME I'LL SOON BE BEATEN BY THE OTHER TRIBES... HMMM! WHAT CAN I DO?

HRMPH!... MAYBE WHO'M I FEAR MOST, COULD UNWITTINGLY GIVE ME A HAND!!

SO ROMULUS REALIZED HIS PLAN TO INCREASE HIS ARMY BY CREATING ON THE CAPITOLINE, THE HILL NEXT TO THE PALATINE, AN ASYLUM THAT IS...

...A NEUTRAL ZONE WHERE ALL THE RENEGADES AND RUNAWAYS FROM THE SURROUNDING TRIBES COULD FIND SHELTER!?!

RIGHT! GUYS LIKE US!!! ROMULUS HAD A GREAT IDEA: WE'LL DEFEND HIS CITY FOR OUR BED AND BOARD!

YEAH BUT... I HEARD THAT ALREADY THERE AREN'T MANY WOMEN AROUND... AND WE'LL FIND NO GIRLS!

I WOULDN'T WORRY ABOUT THIS TOO MUCH, ROMULUS IS A CLEVER GUY...

...AND I'M SURE HE'S ALREADY FOUND A SOLUTION!

INDEED...

DON'T WORRY: I'M CALLING A PARTY, WE'LL INVITE THE SABINES WITH THEIR FAMILIES AND AS SOON AS THEY ARRIVE...

WE'LL KIDNAP THEIR WOMEN...

...SHELTER FOR ROBBERS AND RUNAWAYS? SAY WHAT YOU WANT ABOUT THE CAPITOL HILL BUT IT'S ALWAYS FASCINATING...

NOW THE MAJESTIC TEMPLE OF CAPITOLINE JUPITER, THE MOST ANCIENT TEMPLE OF ROME PRESIDES ON TOP OF THE HILL...

...WE HAVE CERTAINLY GONE A LONG WAY!

29

...AND SO WHERE THERE ONCE WAS ONLY MUD AND SLIME THERE ROSE A GREAT SQUARE FIRST WITH ONLY A SIMPLE MARKET BUT SLOWLY BUT SURELY IT GREW WITH TABERNAE WHERE ONE COULD EAT AND TRADE

FOR THE TIME BEING TODAY WE FINISHED THE ROOF... LET'S GET DOWN!

I REALLY CAN'T IMAGINE THE FORUM AS A MARSHY SWAMP...

WELL MUCH TIME HAS GONE BY

THE CONSTRUCTION OF TABERNAE WAS THE FIRST STEP, THEN THE FIRST TEMPLES AND HONORARY COLUMNS WERE BUILT... AND THE FORUM KEPT ON BEING ENRICHENED...

...SO THE MARKET WAS MOVED AND THE TABERNAE WERE SET INTO THE PORTICOES OF THE BASILICAE AND THEY NOW ONLY TRADE IN LUXURY PRODUCTS...

...AND SO WHERE THERE ONCE WAS ONLY MUD AND SLIME THERE ROSE A GREAT SQUARE FIRST WITH ONLY A SIMPLE MARKET BUT SLOWLY BUT SURELY IT GREW WITH TABERNAE WHERE ONE COULD EAT AND TRADE

FOR THE TIME BEING TODAY WE FINISHED THE ROOF... LET'S GET DOWN!

I REALLY CAN'T IMAGINE THE FORUM AS A MARSHY SWAMP...

WELL MUCH TIME HAS GONE BY

THE CONSTRUCTION OF TABERNAE WAS THE FIRST STEP, THEN THE FIRST TEMPLES AND HONORARY COLUMNS WERE BUILT... AND THE FORUM KEPT ON BEING ENRICHENED...

...SO THE MARKET WAS MOVED AND THE TABERNAE WERE SET INTO THE PORTICOES OF THE BASILICAE AND THEY NOW ONLY TRADE IN LUXURY PRODUCTS...

...AND SO WHERE THERE ONCE WAS ONLY MUD AND SLIME THERE ROSE A GREAT SQUARE FIRST WITH ONLY A SIMPLE MARKET BUT SLOWLY BUT SURELY IT GREW WITH TABERNAE WHERE ONE COULD EAT AND TRADE

FOR THE TIME BEING TODAY WE FINISHED THE ROOF... LET'S GET DOWN!

WELL MUCH TIME HAS GONE BY

I REALLY CAN'T IMAGINE THE FORUM AS A MARSHY SWAMP...

THE CONSTRUCTION OF TABERNAE WAS THE FIRST STEP, THEN THE FIRST TEMPLES AND HONORARY COLUMNS WERE BUILT... AND THE FORUM KEPT ON BEING ENRICHENED...

...SO THE MARKET WAS MOVED AND THE TABERNAE WERE SET INTO THE PORTICOES OF THE BASILICAE AND THEY NOW ONLY TRADE IN LUXURY PRODUCTS...

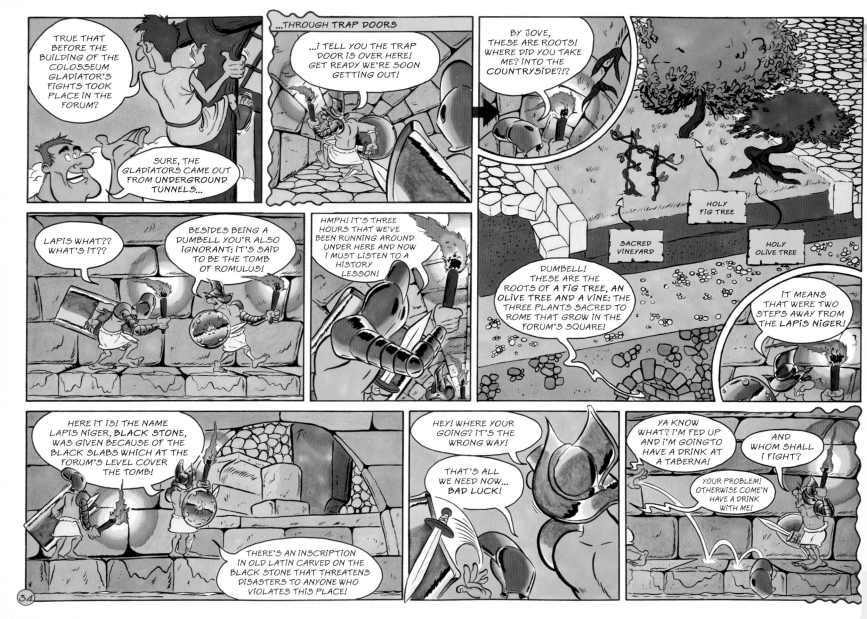

BUT THINK OF THOSE POOR SLOBS WHO HAD TO BUILD THE CLOACA MAXIMA: REAL HEROES... WITH ALL THAT STINK!

T'WAS BETTER TO BUILD THE ROSTRA PLATFORM! THINK OF SETTING THE ROSTRA INTO THE WALL!

THE ROSTRA WAS A VERY IMPORTANT PLATFORM FROM WHERE GREAT ROMANS SPOKE TO THE CROWD! IN THOSE HOLES, THERE WERE THE...

...ROSTRA, THE BRONZE SPURS TAKEN FROM ENEMY SHIPS' PROWS DESTROYED BY THE ROMAN ARMY, WHAT AN HONOUR!

YEAH! OUR ARMY WAS INVINCIBLE ALSO ON THE SEAS! THINK OF THE PUNIC WARS...

...WHICH WE WON THANKS TO OUR SHIP'S ROSTRAE!

WOW! I DIDN'T KNOW THAT YOU FOUGHT IN THE PUNIC WARS!?! GOSH! THEN YOU MUST BE A GHOST!

YOU'R KIDDING... BUT LET ME TELL YOU THAT LAST NIGHT NEAR THE MUNDUS, I... SAW CAESAR'S GHOST!!!!

...HE NEVER SAW COMPLETED, POOR GUY!

HERE'S THE WAY THE CURIA LOOKS LIKE TODAY, THE NEW SEAT OF THE SENATE, WANTED BY CAESAR AND THAT HE NEVER SAW COMPLETED BECAUSE HE WAS BRUTALLY MURDERED BY CONSPIRATORS ON MARCH 15TH 44 BC OUR FRIEND THE CENTURION REMEMBERS THE FACTS...

THIS IS THE UMBILICUS URBIS IT MARKED THE CENTER OF ROME; INSIDE THERE WAS A CAVITY (THE MUNDUS) SAID TO LINK THE WORLD OF THE LIVING WITH THAT OF THE... DEAD! HUUUUUH!!

HA!HA! HA! IF CAESAR'S LOOKING FOR YOU... MAYBE YOU OWED HIM MONEY!

SHUT UP! DON'T FOOL WITH THE DEAD! JULIUS CAESAR DID A LOT FOR ROME, MAKING THE FORUM BIGGER! THINK OF THE NEW SENATE THAT...

35

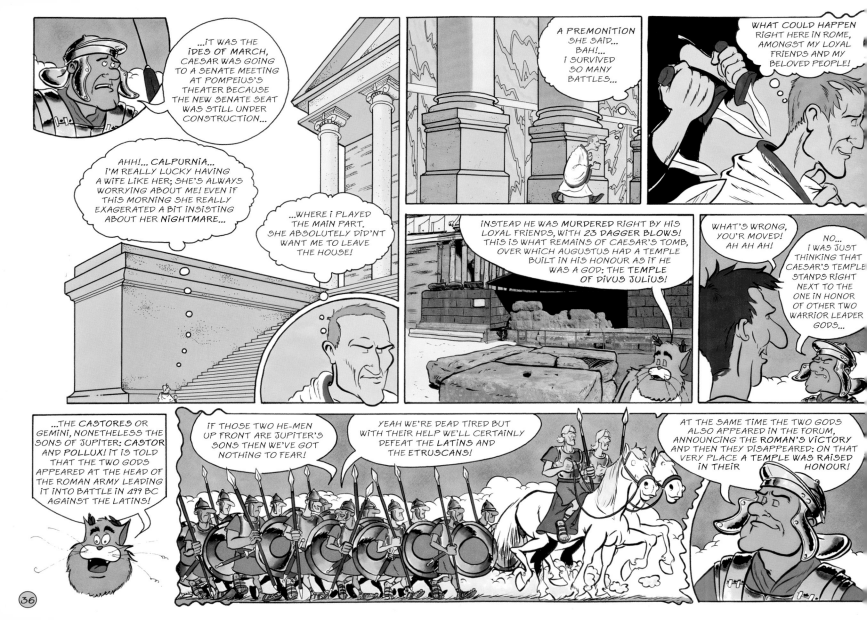

SURE, YOU SOLDIERS RISK YOUR SKINS (EXCEPT YOU, HERE) BUT AT LEAST YOU RECEIVE YOUR PAY! WE SLOG AWAY ALL DAY LONG AND W'VE NOT YET SEEN A SESTERTIUM!

SO DO AS CAESAR; GO AND GET THEM AT THE TEMPLE OF SATURN WHERE THE ROMAN TREASURY IS KEPT!

WITH THE SUBTLE DIFFERENCE THAT YOUR CAESAR TOOK THE MONEY HIGH HANDED WHEREAS I HAVE THE RIGHT TO THEM!!

TRUE! BUT REMEMBER THAT CAESAR TOOK THAT MONEY TO DEFEAT HIS RIVAL POMPEIUS, HE DID IT FOR THE SAKE OF ROME!

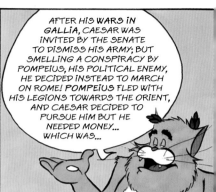

AFTER HIS WARS IN GALLIA, CAESAR WAS INVITED BY THE SENATE TO DISMISS HIS ARMY; BUT SMELLING A CONSPIRACY BY POMPEIUS, HIS POLITICAL ENEMY, HE DECIDED INSTEAD TO MARCH ON ROME! POMPEIUS FLED WITH HIS LEGIONS TOWARDS THE ORIENT, AND CAESAR DECIDED TO PURSUE HIM BUT HE NEEDED MONEY... WHICH WAS...

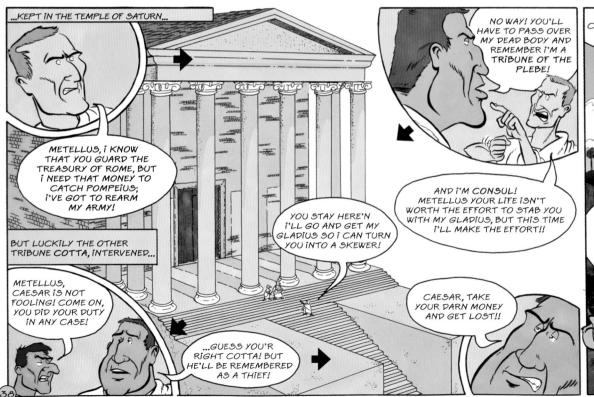

...KEPT IN THE TEMPLE OF SATURN...

METELLUS, I KNOW THAT YOU GUARD THE TREASURY OF ROME, BUT I NEED THAT MONEY TO CATCH POMPEIUS; I'VE GOT TO REARM MY ARMY!

NO WAY! YOU'LL HAVE TO PASS OVER MY DEAD BODY AND REMEMBER I'M A TRIBUNE OF THE PLEBE!

AND I'M CONSUL! METELLUS YOUR LIFE ISN'T WORTH THE EFFORT TO STAB YOU WITH MY GLADIUS, BUT THIS TIME I'LL MAKE THE EFFORT!!

BUT LUCKILY THE OTHER TRIBUNE COTTA, INTERVENED...

YOU STAY HERE'N I'LL GO AND GET MY GLADIUS SO I CAN TURN YOU INTO A SKEWER!

METELLUS, CAESAR IS NOT FOOLING! COME ON, YOU DID YOUR DUTY IN ANY CASE!

CAESAR, TAKE YOUR DARN MONEY AND GET LOST!!

...GUESS YOU'R RIGHT COTTA! BUT HE'LL BE REMEMBERED AS A THIEF!

...TRUE THAT METELLUS CAST A SPELL ON CAESAR!! BUT IN THE END HE WAS ONLY DOING HIS DUTY TO PROTECT THE STATE TREASURY...

...WHICH WAS KEPT IN THE TEMPLE OF SATURN, RIGHT BEHIND ME! IT WAS BUILT IN 498 BC AND SUBSEQUENTLY RESTORED IN 42 BC AND GUESS BY WHOM? BY CAESAR HIMSELF!!! THE BOTTOM LINE IS THAT HE PAID BACK THE MONEY HE HAD TAKEN...

...EMBELLISHING THE TEMPLE BUT...

38

...THEN AUGUSTUS RAISED THAT COLUMN IN FRONT OF THE TEMPLE WHICH, IN MY VIEW DOESN'T LOOK WELL AT ALL!

YA MEAN THE COLUMN OF THE MILIARIUM AUREUM? IT'S VERY USEFUL: THE DISTANCES BETWEEN ROME AND THE MOST IMPORTANT CITIES OF THE EMPIRE ARE WRITTEN THERE!

WHEN Y'VE GOT TO GO ON VACATION, YOU LOOK AT THE COLUMN AND...

...WHAT'Y A MEAN VACATION!! PATRICIANS MAYBE... BUT US PLEBEIANS WE'RE ALWAYS HERE AT THE GRINDSTONE!!! THERE SHOULD BE ANOTHER REVOLT OF THE PLEBE: IT'S ALL THE FAULT OF THAT GUY MENENIUS AGRIPPA!

....

MENENIUS AGRIPPA WAS A ROMAN PATRICIAN, VERY DIPLOMATIC, WHO IN 494 BC PREVENTED THE FIRST STRIKE IN ROMAN HISTORY! HE CONVINCED THE REVOLTED PLEBEIANS WHO HAD LEFT THE CITY TO COME BACK THANKS...

...TO HIS SPEACH WHICH HAS BECOME A LEGEND!

...BECAUSE ROME IS LIKE A HUMAN BODY: YOU PLEBEIANS ARE THE HANDS THAT FEED THE STOMACH, THAT IS THE PATRICIANS AND THE SENATE, THE STOMACH IN TURN, THANKS TO YOUR FOOD, BRINGS ENERGY TO THE WHOLE BODY: IF THE HANDS STOPPED WORKING THE BODY WOULD DIE!!

THEREFORE PLEBEIANS AND PATRICIANS, HANDS AND BELLY OF THE SAME BODY, CAN GO ON LIVING ONLY IF THEY DO SO IN HARMONY!

I GUESS YOU UNDERSTAND THAT HERE IN THE FORUM EVERY BUILDING HAS A STORY TO TELL. TEMPLES WERE USUALLY BUILT TO REMEMBER AN EVENT OR TO CELEBRATE A PERSON, LIKE THE TEMPLE OF VESPASIAN (OR WHAT REMAINS OF IT) BACK HERE, RAISED BY EMPEROR TITUS IN MEMORY OF HIS FATHER!

HOWEVER, AS WE SAW THERE WERE ALSO OTHER IMPORTANT BUILDINGS FOR IMPORTANT CIVIL AND RELIGIOUS FUNCTIONS AS...

WELL, IN THE END IT'S ALSO THANKS TO HIM THAT WE BEGAN HAVING OUR REPRESENTATIVES IN THE STATE'S HIGH POSITIONS. THE TRIBUNES OF THE PLEBEIANS, ENJOYING POLITICAL IMMUNITY!

...YEAH SO HIGH AND INVIOLABLE THAT ANY CAESAR GUY CAN THREATEN THEM WITH DEATH!

FOR YEARS THE PLEBEIANS CONTINUED TO FIGHT FOR THEIR RIGHTS AS CITIZENS. FINALLY PEACE WAS REACHED AND TO REMEMBER IT IN 367 BC THE TEMPLE OF CONCORD WAS BUILT IN THE FORUM RIGHT HERE WHERE THERE'S ONLY GRASS NOW!

40

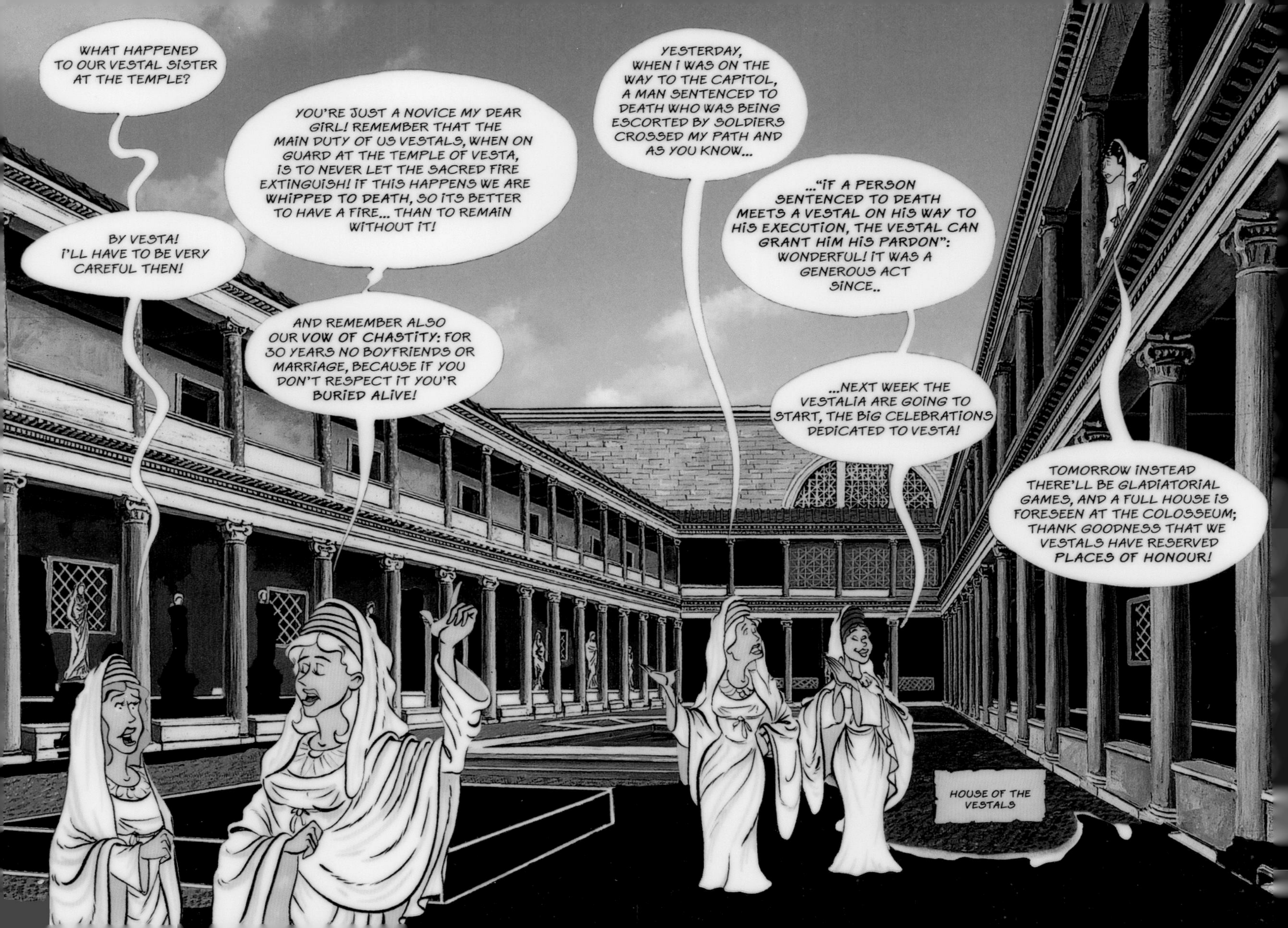
WHAT HAPPENED TO OUR VESTAL SISTER AT THE TEMPLE?
YOU'RE JUST A NOVICE MY DEAR GIRL! REMEMBER THAT THE MAIN DUTY OF US VESTALS, WHEN ON GUARD AT THE TEMPLE OF VESTA, IS TO NEVER LET THE SACRED FIRE EXTINGUISH! IF THIS HAPPENS WE ARE WHIPPED TO DEATH, SO ITS BETTER TO HAVE A FIRE... THAN TO REMAIN WITHOUT IT!
BY VESTA! I'LL HAVE TO BE VERY CAREFUL THEN!
AND REMEMBER ALSO OUR VOW OF CHASTITY: FOR 30 YEARS NO BOYFRIENDS OR MARRIAGE, BECAUSE IF YOU DON'T RESPECT IT YOU'R BURIED ALIVE!
YESTERDAY, WHEN I WAS ON THE WAY TO THE CAPITOL, A MAN SENTENCED TO DEATH WHO WAS BEING ESCORTED BY SOLDIERS CROSSED MY PATH AND AS YOU KNOW...
..."IF A PERSON SENTENCED TO DEATH MEETS A VESTAL ON HIS WAY TO HIS EXECUTION, THE VESTAL CAN GRANT HIM HIS PARDON": WONDERFUL! IT WAS A GENEROUS ACT SINCE..
...NEXT WEEK THE VESTALIA ARE GOING TO START, THE BIG CELEBRATIONS DEDICATED TO VESTA!
TOMORROW INSTEAD THERE'LL BE GLADIATORIAL GAMES, AND A FULL HOUSE IS FORESEEN AT THE COLOSSEUM; THANK GOODNESS THAT WE VESTALS HAVE RESERVED PLACES OF HONOUR!
HOUSE OF THE VESTALS

POOR VESTALS! YOU'R COMPLAINING, INSTEAD YOU'R LUCKY TO HAVE THIS JOB: ITS QUIET AND ALWAYS IN OPEN AIR... THINK ABOUT THOSE WHO WORK CLOSED UP IN THE...

...TABULARIUM, THE STATE ARCHIVES BUILT IN 80 BC TO SAFEGUARD LAWS AND PUBLIC DOCUMENTS! JUST FOR SAKE OF HISTORICAL CONTINUITY... NOWADAYS IN THE UPPER PART... THERE IS ROME'S TOWN HALL!

LOOK WHO'S TALKING! YOU PREACH WELL... NOT DOING ANYTHING ALL DAY... AND AT THE TABULARIUM THEY'RE NOT BREAKING THEIR BACKS THE WAY WE ARE

LOOK INSIDE IT'S REALLY TOUGH GOING ...

...MANY OF THE LAWS AND ACTS OF ROME ARE ENGRAVED ON BRONZE PLATES, SO YOU'VE GOT TO BE IN GOOD SHAPE TO WORK AT THE TABULARIUM! A LOT OF GUYS GET TIRED QUICKLY!

GOING ON VISITING THE FORUM, UNDER THE TABULARIUM WE FIND AN ARCH ERECTED IN 202 AD IN HONOUR OF SEPTIMIUS SEVERUS AND OF HIS SONS GETA AND CARACALLA. SOME OF THE DECORATIONS ON THE ARCH HAVE BEEN ERASED... BECAUSE...

...CARACALLA...

WITH THIS DAGGER I KILLED BY BROTHER GETA; WE COULD NOT RULE TOGETHER! NOW THAT I'M THE ONE AND ONLY EMPEROR I ORDER THAT...

...THE NAME OF GETA BE ERASED FROM ALL OF THE ROMAN MONUMENTS: PRETORIANS ARM YOURSELVES...

...WITH CHISELS AND HAMMERS AND START FROM THE ARCH DEDICATED TO MY FATHER!

CARACALLA WANTS ROMANS TO FORGET GETA AND REMAIN ONLY BY HIMSELF IN ROMAN HISTORY!

YEAH BUT IN MY VIEW HE'LL GO DOWN IN HISTORY AS A COMPLETE NUT AND MURDERER!

WHY IS IT ALWAYS UP TO US TO DO THE DIRTY WORK?

...AND SO SOME INSCRIPTIONS WERE CANCELLED FROM THE ARCH OF SEPTIMIUS SEVERUS AND... CARACALLA WENT DOWN IN HISTORY FOR HIS... AHEM... PECULIAR CHARACTER

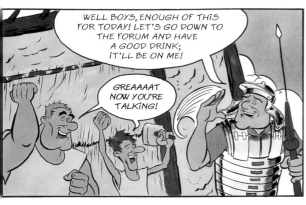

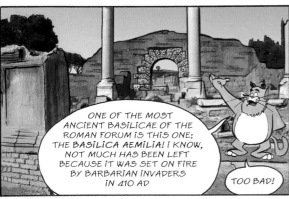

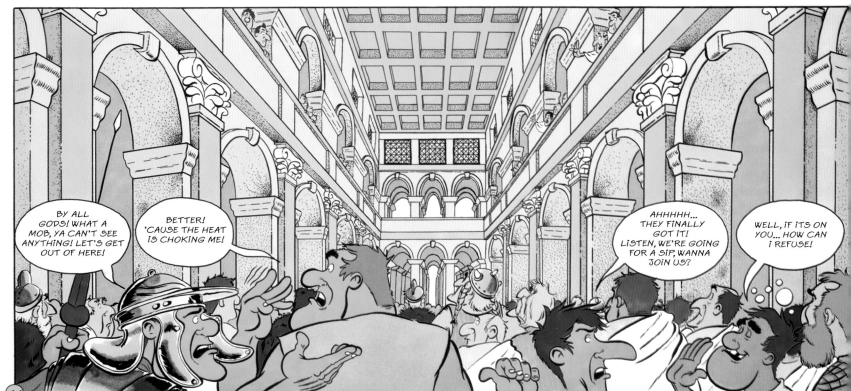

DURING THE CENTURIES THAT MADE ROME BIG, OTHER MONUMENTS WERE BUILT IN THE FORUM THAT Y'A CAN STILL SEE TODAY: FOR INSTANCE NEAR THE BASILICA AEMILIA THERE'S...

...THIS TEMPLE DEDICATED BY EMPEROR ANTONINUS TO HIS WIFE FAUSTINA WHEN SHE DIED; THE SENATE, WHEN HE PASSED AWAY, EXTENDED THE DEDICATION TO HIM AS WELL (TO SAVE A COIN?)!

NEXT TO THE TEMPLE OF ANTONINUS AND FAUSTINA YA CAN SEE THE LITTLE TEMPLE TO DIVUS ROMULUS! NOTHING TO DO WITH THE MYTHICAL FOUNDER OF ROME, THIS ROMULUS WAS THE SON OF EMPEROR MAXENTIUS!

HERE, IN THE MIDDLE OF THE SQUARE, STANDS THE LAST HONORARY COLUMN ERECTED IN 608 AD IN THE PRACTICALLY, BY THEN, ABANDONED FORUM. SEEMS WAS DEDICATED TO THE BYZANTINE EMPEROR PHOCAS. OBVIOUSLY IT IS AN OLD COLUMN REEEEEEECYCLED!

WALKING ALONG THE VIA SACRA TOWARDS THE ARCH OF TITUS, WE SEE ON THE WAY THE ENORMOUS BASILICA OF MAXENTIUS. IT WAS STARTED BY MAXENTIUS IN 306 AD BUT COMPLETED BY CONSTANTINE IN 312 AD AFTER HE DEFEATED MAXENTIUS IN THE MYTHICAL BATTLE AT THE MILVIUS BRIDGE! A BIT COMPLICATED THESE ROMANS HUH!?!!

CLOSE TO THE ARCH OF SEPTIMIUS SEVERUS, AT THE FOOT OF THE CAPITOL, THERE'S THE PORTICO OF THE CONSENTING GODS: THE 12 MAIN GODS THAT ACCORDING TO ROMAN MYTHOLOGY WERE TO ADVISE POOR JUPITER!

AFTER THE FALL OF THE ROMAN EMPIRE, IN THE COURSE OF CENTURIES, THE FORUM WAS ABANDONED AND SACKED... SLOWLY IT SILTED IN AND WAS COVERED WITH GRASS TO THE POINT THAT ROMANS, UNTIL ABOUT 1870 USED IT FOR CATTLE GRAZING AND SO IT WAS CALLED "CAMPO VACCINO" (FROM THE ITALIAN, VACCA, COW)...

...AND TO THINK THAT ONCE, NEAR THIS ARCH, TRIUMPHANT ROMAN GENERALS PARADED RETURNING FROM THEIR CONQUESTS AND FESTIVE CROWDS CHEERED THEM!

OVER THERE, MOST PROBABLY, JULIUS CAESAR SPOKE TO THE CROWDS!

OH RUGANTINO... HOW MANY THINGS YOU KNOW, C'MON TELL ME MORE, I'M HANGING ON YOUR EVERY WORD!!

WELL, JUST IMAGINE THAT ON THE PALATINE HILL THERE WAS THE HUT OF ROMULUS THE MYTHICAL FOUNDER OF ROME, THAT WAS SAFEGUARDED FOR CENTURIES BECAUSE LABORERS REPAIRED IT CONTINUOUSLY!

HOW COME YOU'R SO SURE THAT ROMULUS'S HUT WAS RIGHT THERE?

EVERYONE KNOWS ABOUT IT... AND I MYSELF PICKED UP WOOD FROM THOSE RUINS TO BUILD A TROUGH FOR MY COWS, YA SHOULD SEE HOW NICE IT LOOKED!

WHAT D'YOU KNOW ABOUT THIS HUT OF ROMULUS! TRUE THAT WORKERS REPAIRED IT CONTINUOUSLY??

NOPE... BUT WHAT CAN I TELL YA... THOSE LABORERS MUST HAVE BEEN POOR LOW LIFE LIKE US!

AT THE BEGINNING OF THE 1900'S CAMPO VACCINO'S AREA WAS EXCAVATED AND THE PRESENT RUINS OF THE FORUM WERE BROUGHT TO LIGHT. BUT THAT'S ANOTHER STORY...

...I'LL TELL YOU BETTER SOME OTHER TIME!

47

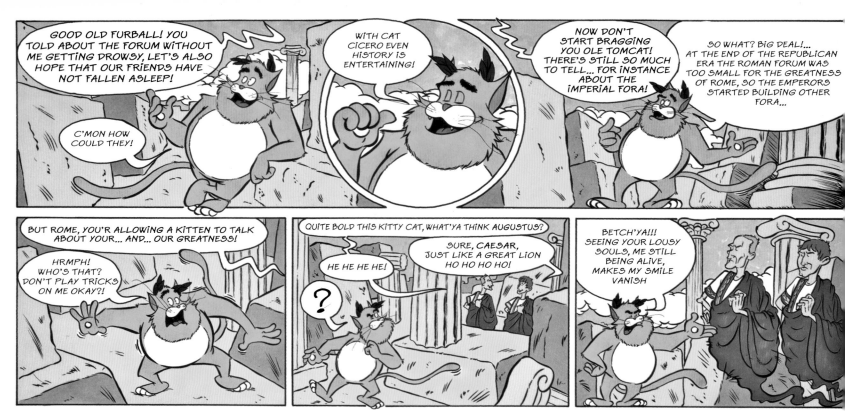

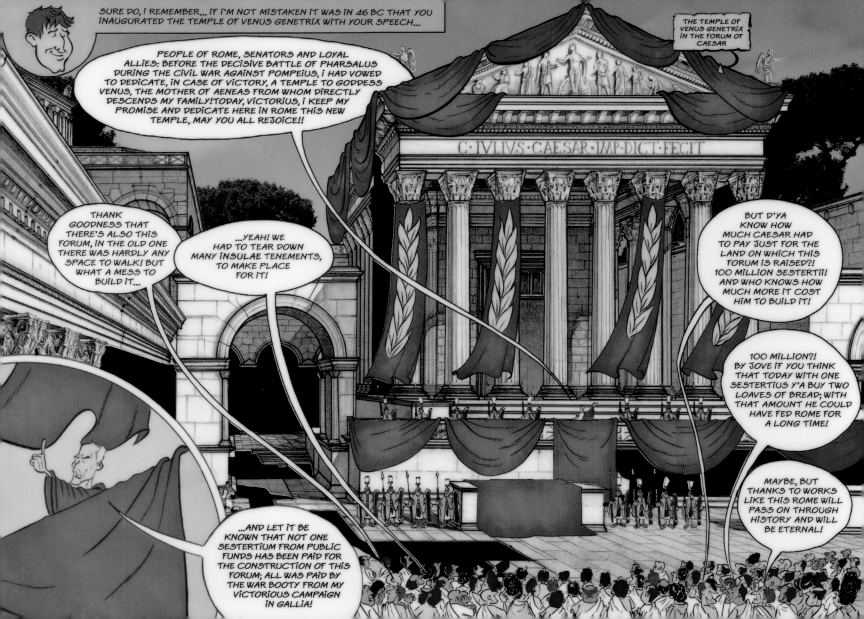

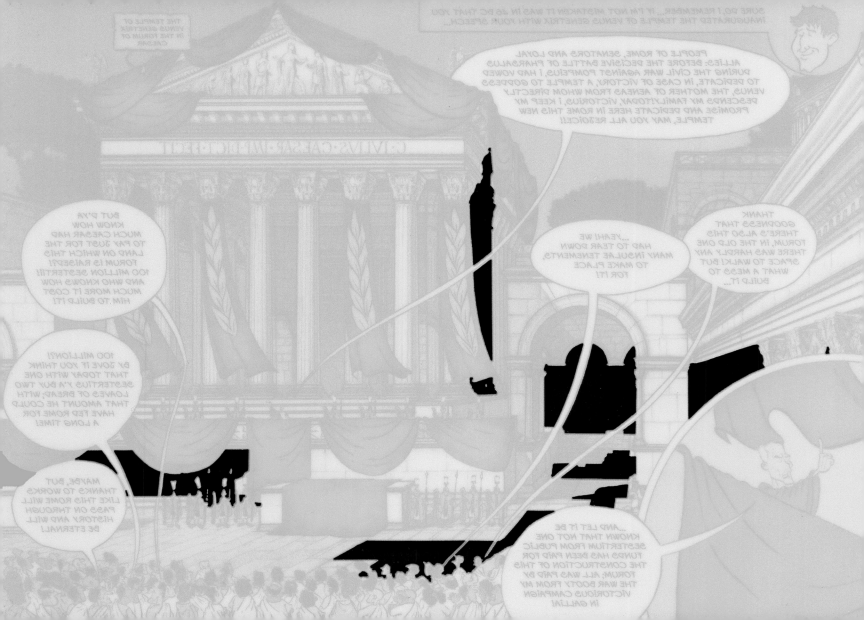

...I REMEMBER WHEN INSIDE THE TEMPLE THERE WAS YOUR STATUE AND CLEOPATRA'S... NOT TO MENTION THE VARIOUS WORKS OF ART THAT WERE KEPT THERE: PAINTINGS, JEWEL COLLECTIONS...

...INDEED! BUT ALSO YOUR FORUM WAS TO BE RECKONED WITH, AUGUSTUS!

SURE... BUT TOO BAD YOU DID'NT LIVE TO SEE IT! IT HAD A RECTANGULAR FORM LIKE YOUR'S, I ONLY ADDED TWO EXEDRAE ON THE SIDES AND DECORATED IT WITH STATUES OF THE GREAT MEN FROM THE PAST!

BY THE WAY, NOT BAD THAT STATUE IN THE SQUARE'S CENTER WHICH SHOWED YOU ON A TRIUMPHAL CHARIOT, CERTAINLY BETTER THAN MINE...

IMAGINE THAT VIRGIL THE POET WAS CRAZY ABOUT IT, I REMEMBER THAT ONCE...

MY DEAR FRIEND VIRGIL, YOU RECALL MY FATHER JULIUS CAESAR SAID THAT OUR FAMILY DESCENDED DIRECTLY FROM AENEAS THE MYTHICAL HERO WHO FLED FROM TROY AND...

...LANDED ON THE COASTS OF LATIUM?! WELL... WHAT DO YOU THINK OF PUTTING IT ALL DOWN BLACK ON WHITE TO MAKE AN IMMORTAL EPIC OF MY NOBLE STOCK?

NOT BAD! I'VE ALREADY GOT AN IDEA... A POEM... IT COULD START WITH AENEAS FLEEING FROM TROY IN FLAMES!

GREAT! RIGHT A WAY A DRAMATIC TURN OF EVENTS!! THAT'S IT VIRGIL, I LIKE IT! GO AHEAD!

WHEN I'LL FINISH THE POEM, O GREAT AUGUSTUS, WILL YOU PLACE A STATUE OF ME LIKE YOUR'S IN THE FORUM'S SQUARE?

NOW COME ON VIRGIL, DON'T GET TOO BIG FOR YOUR BOOTS!

OUR FAMILY HAS MADE ROME GREAT, BUT VIRGIL MADE IT IMMORTAL, THANKS TO YOU AUGUSTUS!

RIGHT! YOU SURE PLEASED ME AND WERE LOYAL WHEN I THINK OF BRUTUS AND CASSIUS...

YOU BET, THEY WERE ONLY ABLE TO... STAB YOU...! WHILE I AVENGED YOU AND MY FORUM IS PROOF!

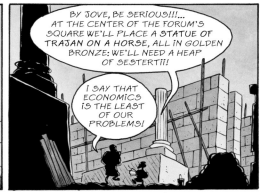

...AND HERE IS YOUR BASILICA! IT THE BIGGEST BUILT SO FAR. IT'S 170 METERS LONG. IT'S RICH IN PRECIOUS MARBLE COLUMNS OF DIFFERENT COLOURS, IN THE TWO EXEDRAE AT EACH END TRIALS WILL TAKE PLACE!

NOT BAD, NOT BAD AT ALL, MY COMPLIMENTS APOLLODORUS! I'LL CALL IT BASILICA ULPIA IN HONOUR OF MY FAMILY: THE ULPIANS!

THANK YOU INFINITELY, O DIVINE!

BESIDES, THIS FORUM IS WORTHY OF MY CONQUESTS! NEVER BEFORE HAS THE ROMAN EMPIRE KNOWN SUCH A VAST EXPANSION: FROM THE HISPANIC COASTS TO THE PERSIAN GULF PASSING THROUGH THE MARE NOSTRUM!

LET'S GO ON WITH THE VISIT, YET FIRST SHOW ME THE WHOLE PLAN OF THE FORUM'S LAYOUT, I WANT TO SEE HOW BIGGER IT IS COMPARED TO THE OTHERS... HO HO HO!

HO, HO, HO

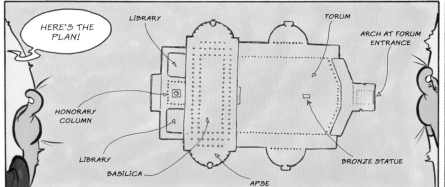

HERE'S THE PLAN!

LIBRARY

FORUM

ARCH AT FORUM ENTRANCE

HONORARY COLUMN

LIBRARY

BASILICA

APSE

BRONZE STATUE

CLIMBING UP THE STAIRS YOU REACH TWO LIBRARIES, ONE GREEK AND ONE LATIN; IN THE INNER COURTYARD YOU CAN ADMIRE... MY MASTERPIECE!

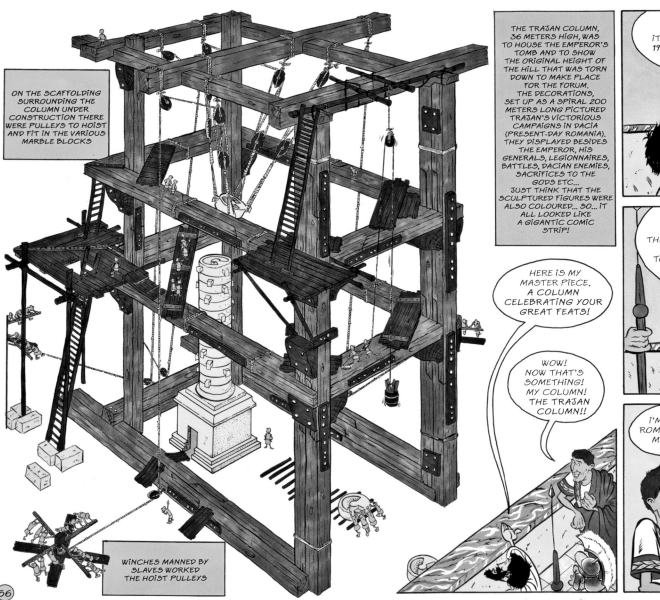

ON THE SCAFFOLDING SURROUNDING THE COLUMN UNDER CONSTRUCTION THERE WERE PULLEYS TO HOIST AND FIT IN THE VARIOUS MARBLE BLOCKS

WINCHES MANNED BY SLAVES WORKED THE HOIST PULLEYS

THE TRAJAN COLUMN, 36 METERS HIGH, WAS TO HOUSE THE EMPEROR'S TOMB AND TO SHOW THE ORIGINAL HEIGHT OF THE HILL THAT WAS TORN DOWN TO MAKE PLACE FOR THE FORUM.
THE DECORATIONS, SET UP AS A SPIRAL 200 METERS LONG PICTURED TRAJAN'S VICTORIOUS CAMPAIGNS IN DACIA (PRESENT-DAY ROMANIA). THEY DISPLAYED BESIDES THE EMPEROR, HIS GENERALS, LEGIONNAIRES, BATTLES, DACIAN ENEMIES, SACRIFICES TO THE GODS ETC...
JUST THINK THAT THE SCULPTURED FIGURES WERE ALSO COLOURED... SO... IT ALL LOOKED LIKE A GIGANTIC COMIC STRIP!

HERE IS MY MASTER PIECE. A COLUMN CELEBRATING YOUR GREAT FEATS!

WOW! NOW THAT'S SOMETHING! MY COLUMN! THE TRAJAN COLUMN!!

SO, MY EMPEROR, ALLOW ME TO SHOW YOU THE DETAILS: IT'S 100 FEET HIGH AND MADE OF 19 VERY PURE MARBLE BLOCKS WEIGHING 31 TONS EACH!

× 19

THE INSIDE IS EMPTY AND WE'RE BUILDING IN THERE A SPIRAL STAIRCASE THAT WILL REACH THE TOP WHERE WE'LL PLACE YOUR BRONZE STATUE!

I'M CERTAIN: ROME WILL LOVE MY FORUM!

SURE, O DIVINE ENTITY... AND EVEN MORE SO THE NEW MARKETS THAT WILL BE BUILT AT THE BACK OF THE FORUM!

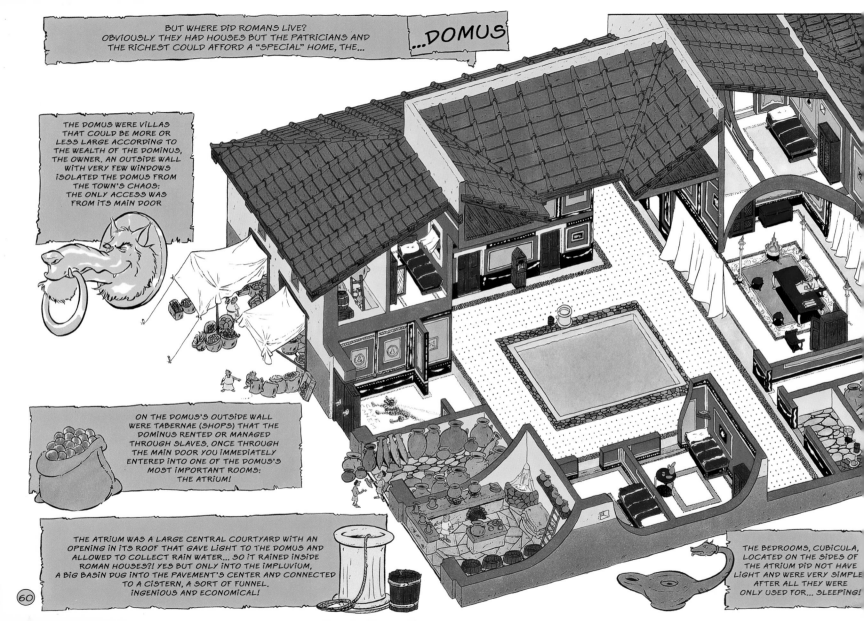

BUT WHERE DID ROMANS LIVE?
OBVIOUSLY THEY HAD HOUSES BUT THE PATRICIANS AND
THE RICHEST COULD AFFORD A "SPECIAL" HOME, THE...

...DOMUS

THE DOMUS WERE VILLAS THAT COULD BE MORE OR LESS LARGE ACCORDING TO THE WEALTH OF THE DOMINUS, THE OWNER. AN OUTSIDE WALL WITH VERY FEW WINDOWS ISOLATED THE DOMUS FROM THE TOWN'S CHAOS: THE ONLY ACCESS WAS FROM ITS MAIN DOOR

ON THE DOMUS'S OUTSIDE WALL WERE TABERNAE (SHOPS) THAT THE DOMINUS RENTED OR MANAGED THROUGH SLAVES. ONCE THROUGH THE MAIN DOOR YOU IMMEDIATELY ENTERED INTO ONE OF THE DOMUS'S MOST IMPORTANT ROOMS: THE ATRIUM!

THE ATRIUM WAS A LARGE CENTRAL COURTYARD WITH AN OPENING IN ITS ROOF THAT GAVE LIGHT TO THE DOMUS AND ALLOWED TO COLLECT RAIN WATER... SO IT RAINED INSIDE ROMAN HOUSES?! YES BUT ONLY INTO THE IMPLUVIUM, A BIG BASIN DUG INTO THE PAVEMENT'S CENTER AND CONNECTED TO A CISTERN, A SORT OF FUNNEL. INGENIOUS AND ECONOMICAL!

THE BEDROOMS, CUBICULA, LOCATED ON THE SIDES OF THE ATRIUM DID NOT HAVE LIGHT AND WERE VERY SIMPLE AFTER ALL THEY WERE ONLY USED FOR... SLEEPING!

AROUND THE COURT THERE RAN A PORTICO DECORATED, BETWEEN ITS COLUMNS, WITH "OSCILLA", SCUPLTURED MARBLE DISKS THAT DANGLED IN THE BREEZE!

USUALLY THE FIRST FLOOR WAS FOR SERVANTS: HERE WERE THE CELLAE SERVORUM, SMALL ROOMS WHERE THE SLAVES FREQUENTLY SLEPT ONE ON TOP OF THE OTHER!

THE KITCHEN, CALLED "CULINA" WAS NOT PARTICULARLY LARGE BECAUSE ROMANS PREFERRED TO EAT OUT IN THE TABERNAE OR THEY WOULD HAVE READY-MADE FOOD BROUGHT IN... BUT NO FAST FOOD: IT HAD NOT BEEN INVENTED YET... FORTUNATELY!!!

IN THE TRICLINIUM, THE DINING ROOM, THE DOMINUS WOULD OFFER HIS GUESTS SUMPTUOUS BANQUETS WHERE ONE ATE, DRANK AND CLOSED POLITICAL OR BUSINESS DEALS. THESE BANQUETS COULD LAST UP TO EIGHT HOURS! THE GUESTS ATE LYING DOWN ON COUCHES PLACED AROUND THE TABLE. FORKS DID NOT YET EXIST AND THEREFORE YOU ATE THE MANY COURSES WITH YOUR HANDS. VERY OFTEN THERE WERE MUSICIANS, DANCERS OR OTHER FORMS OF ENTERTAINMENT...

PASSING THROUGH THE TABLINIUM, YOU ENTERED INTO THE PERISTYLIUM, A BEAUTIFUL INNER COURTYARD DECORATED WITH PLANTS AND FLOWERS WHERE MANY TIMES THERE WAS A BASIN IN THE CENTER! JUST IMAGINE HOW NICE IT MUST HAVE BEEN TO STROLL AMONG CYPRUS TREES, OLEANDERS, SUMPTUOUS STATUES AND DECORATED COLUMNS... NOT BAD EH!!

AT THE DOMUS'S CENTER THERE WAS OFTEN THE DOMINUS'S PRIVATE STUDY FROM WHERE THE DOMINUS MANAGED HIS BUSINESS, RECEIVED HIS FRIENDS AND MET HIS PROTÉGÉS, HIS "CLIENTES" WHO CALLED HIM "PATRONUS" PATRON, PROTECTOR!

...MORE OR LESS THIS IS HOW THE DAY OF A DOMINUS STARTED!

ITS DAWN? WOW! I REALLY HAD A GOOD NIGHT'S SLEEP!

FIRST OF ALL I MUST PRAY TO MY LARAE, THE DIVINITIES PROTECTING MY HOUSE, IT BETTER TO KEEP THEM ON YOUR SIDE! SLAVE PREPARE THE OFFERINGS!

HERE THEY ARE MASTER: THERE IS ALSO INCENSE TO BURN!

DON'T GIVE ME THAT SKEPTICAL SMIRK CICALONUS: THANKS TO MY LARAE'S PROTECTION WE HAVE A GREAT LIFE HERE AND I CAN AFFORD TO PAY YOU!

AFTER SAYING HIS PRAYERS HE GETS DRESSED... DON'T BE SURPRISED IF YOU SEE HIM PUT HIS TOGA OVER THE TUNIC WHICH HE SLEPT IN ALL NIGHT, IN THOSE TIMES...

...THAT'S WHAT YOU DID...

TO PUT ON YOUR 5 METER LONG TOGA, YOU HAD TO BE VERY... VERY... VERY... PATIENT...

PHEW! PUTTING ON THIS TOGA DRIVES ME NUTS!

TODAY LET'S SEE HOW LONG IT WILL TAKE HIM...

I'M ALREADY ALL MESSED UP... DARN HIM AND THIS... THING!

HE'S ALREADY ALL WRAPPED UP... DARN IT!!

PHEW!... THE WORST IS OVER... BUT IF I DON'T FINISH THIS GUY WILL BURST...

IF HE DOESN'T FINISH PUTTING ON THIS TOGA, I'LL GO MAD!!!

TO BEGIN ONE'S MORNING LIKE THIS IS REALLY TIRESOME!!

PANT... PANT... I'M IN PIECES! COULDN'T THEY INVENT SOMETHING MORE PRACTICAL!?

IN THE PATRICIAN DOMUS, HUSBAND AND WIFE DID NOT SLEEP IN THE SAME BED, BUT IN SEPARATE ROOMS...

GOOD MORNING SWEET WIFE, FOR HOW LONG HAVE YOU BEEN SITTING THERE TO... GET READY TO GO?

ONLY THREE HOURS, DEAR, TODAY I'M IN A... HURRY!

DOMINUS, I'M READY WHEN YOU WANT...

DON'T I LOOK GREAT?!

AHEM! I'VE GOT TO GO...

IT'S TIME TO GET A SHAVE AND GET COMBED; OBVIOUSLY PATRICIANS HAD THEIR HOUSE BARBER...

DOMINUS, I RESPECTFULLY POINT OUT THAT THERE ARE SOME WHITE HAIRS, WE SHOULD USE SOME DYE...

HUMPF... YEAH! ALWAYS BETTER THAN GETTING BALD, DON'T YOU THINK SO INSOLENT SLAVE?

HEY DID YOU NOTICE! HE GOT UP, PRAYED, DRESSED, SHAVED AND GOT COMBED AND NOW HE'LL HAVE BREAKFAST BUT THE GUY DIDN'T WASH!! INDEED ROMANS USUALLY DIDN'T HAVE SHOWERS OR TUBS BUT THEY WASHED THEMSELVES OUTSIDE THE HOUSE IN THE PUBLIC BATHS, THE "THERMAE"...

...BUT LET'S GET BACK TO BREAKFAST: FOR THE ROMANS IT WAS ESSENTIAL, MORE SO THAN LUNCH AS IT HAD TO GIVE THEM ENERGY FOR THE WHOLE DAY!

CRUNCH... CRUNCH... CICALONUS... AREN'T THERE SOME CHICKENS LEFT OVER FROM LAST NIGHT'S DINNER?

SURE! I'LL RUSH TO GET THEM!

BURP... BY BACCHUS, WHAT A SLAP-UP MEAL! TO DIGEST I'D BETTER TAKE A WALK TO THE FORUM... I ALSO HAVE A COUPLE OF DEALS TO MAKE THERE...

SORRY DOMINUS, I'M AFRAID YOU'VE GOT TO POSTPONE YOUR WALK BECAUSE OUTSIDE THERE ARE ALREADY SOME CLIENTES...

THE CLIENTES WERE ROMANS OF A LOWER CLASS THAT CAME TO ASK FOR INTRODUCTIONS OR MONEY FROM THE PATRONUS IN EXCHANGE FOR FAVOURS OR... VOTES IN ELECTIONS!

BY JOVE WHY ARE THEY TAKING SO LONG TO LET US IN!

THE PATRONUS LIKES TO EAT A LOT FOR BREAKFAST BUT HE IS ALWAYS VERY GENEROUS, HAVE FAITH!!

I NEED SOME STRINGS TO BE PULLED: I WANT TO JOIN THE PRAETORIANS, WITH MY MUSCLES AND LOOKS...

I INSTEAD WANT TO ASK THE PATRONUS TO GET A QUIET JOB FOR MY SON, HOPEFULLY AT THE TABULARIUM...

...BUT IF HE NOTICES THAT THE DEAL WE WANT TO OFFER HIM IS A CON?

DON'T WORRY, THAT GUY ONLY HAS A FLAIR FOR FOOD BUT NONE FOR BUSINESS!

HERE IS THE "SALUTATIO" WHEN THE CLIENTES MEETS HIS PATRONUS TO...

I PAY YOU MY DEEPEST RESPECTS, PATRONUS, I'M TERRIBLY POOR, WITHOUT A JOB AND HAVE A FAMILY...

OK NOW WE'LL SEE WHAT WE CAN DO... IN THE MEANTIME... CICALONUS... DON'T WE HAVE SOME CHICKEN LEFT OVER FOR THIS GOOD MAN?...

NOPE, ...WE... FINISHED EVERYTHING AT... BREAKFAST!

WELL THEN, LISTEN, I'LL FIND YOU A NICE LITTLE JOB AS A FARMER IN ONE OF MY SENATOR FIRENDS'S VILLAS, WHAT DO YOU THINK ABOUT IT?

OHH! I'LL BE GRATEFUL 'TIL MY LAST DAY!

YEAH, BUT BESIDES BEING GRATEFUL, WHEN I WILL BE SEEKING TO BE CONSUL, YOU WILL DO EVERYTHING YOU CAN TO BRING ME ALL OF YOUR FRIENDS' VOTES!

OOPS! I'VE GOT MYSELF INTO A MESS!

THE INSULA

BUT THE GOOD LIFE WAS FOR ONLY A FEW! THE GREATER PART OF ROME'S INHABITANTS, NOT BEING ABLE TO AFFORD SUCH A HOUSE LIKE A DOMUS, LIVED IN "INSULAE", LARGE APARTMENT COMPLEXES SIMILAR TO TODAY'S LOW-INCOME TENEMENT CONDOMINIUMS

USUALLY THESE BIG TENEMENTS BELONGED TO A WELL TO DO ROMAN WHO RENTED THE VARIOUS APARTMENTS, CALLED "CENACULA", AND ALL THE TABERNAE ON THE GROUND FLOOR.

THE OWNER FREQUENTLY LIVED IN HIS OWNED INSULA, ON THE FIRST FLOOR, IN AN APARTMENT THAT RECALLED A SMALL SCALE DOMUS, ... OBVIOUSLY WITHOUT A GARDEN OR AN IMPLUVIUM

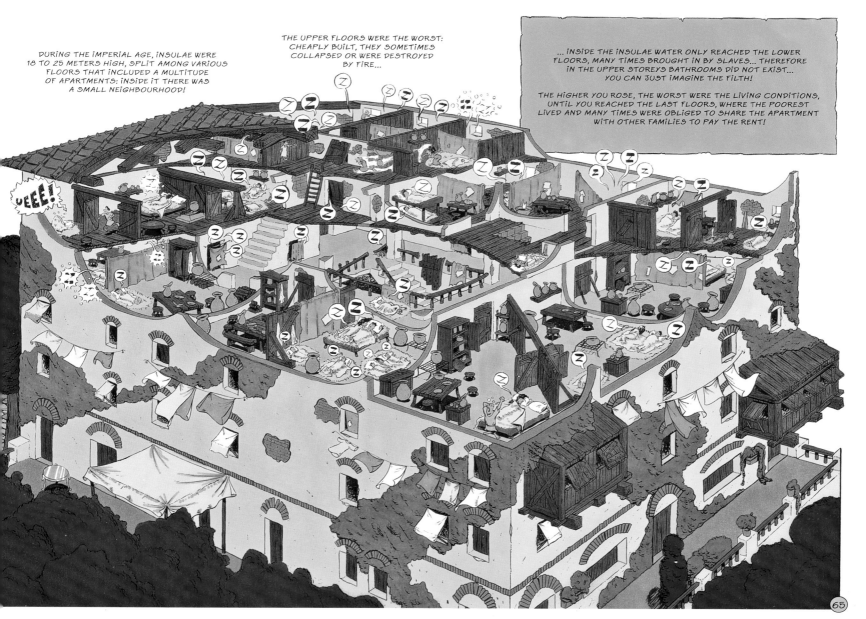

THE LIFE OF A PLEBEIAN WHO LIVED IN THE LAST FLOORS OF AN INSULA WAS QUITE DIFFERENT... ALREADY WHEN HE WOKE UP...

COME ON GET UP!

GASP! BY MARS, THE BARBARIANS ARE ATTACKING!

OH! IT'S ONLY YOU! YOU MADE ME JUMP OUT OF MY SKIN! WHAT'YA WANT? DO YOU KNOW WHAT TIME IT IS?

COME ON YOU LAZY BUM, IT'S SUNRISE AND IT'S TIME YOU GET MOVING TO GO AND WORK!

DON'T MAKE SUCH A FUSS, I'M GOING, I'M GOING...

I MARRIED A NUT! SHE KICKS ME OUT TO GO 'N WORK WITHOUT GIVING ME A BITE... BUT HOW LONG CAN THIS GO ON...

HI!

UMPF!

O.K. I'LL TRY TO SCROUNGE BREAKFAST SOMEWHERE...

BUT YET MY WIFE IS RIGHT, IF I DON'T WORK WE WILL BE KICKED OUT AND WE WILL END UP...

(...LIKE THESE GUYS); HEY! I'M GOING OUT, DO Y'A NEED ANYTHING?

YEAH! HOPEFULLY SOME SESTERTII: UNTIL WE PAY OUR RENT THE LAND LORD WILL KEEP US WALLED UP INSIDE OUR HOUSE LIKE THIS!

WELL IF I SEE THAT AWFUL GUY I'LL TELL HIM THAT IT WILL BE HARD FOR YOU TO EARN SOMETHING WHILE BEING CLOSED UP INSIDE!

NOW THAT'S AN IDEA!

NO NEED TO SAY IT!

GULP

THAT AWFUL GUY IS HERE! IT'S BETTER THAT YOU CUT IT OUT, BECAUSE SHORTLY WE'LL BE COLLECTING RENTS AND I HAVE THE FEELING THAT YOU AND YOUR FAMILY WILL END UP IN THE STREETS!

66

67

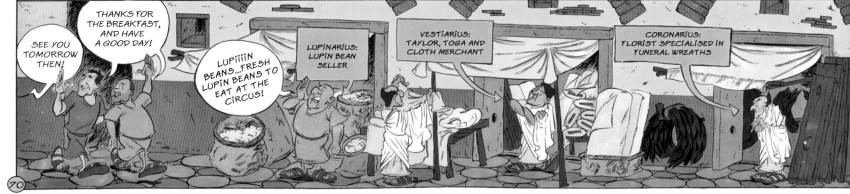

70

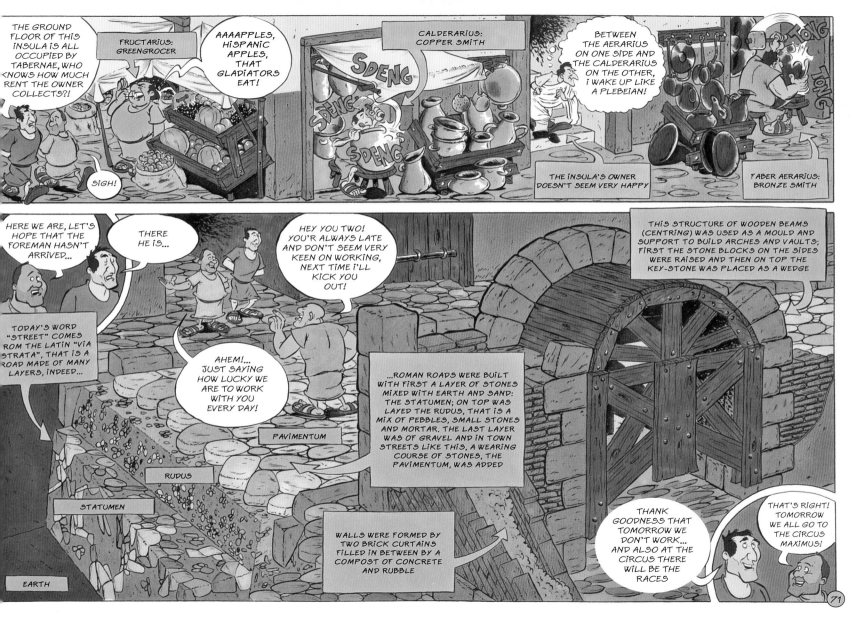

75

DARN RED, I BET A BUNCH OF SESTERTII ON HIM... AND HE SNAPS HIS REINS!!

DON'T GET UPSET, DEAR, THESE THINGS HAPPEN!

SURE I'M ANGRY!! HE WAS SINGLED UP AS THE WINNER, "THE GREAT GERMANIC AURIGA" HE MUST ONLY THANK THE GREEN DRIVER WITHOUT WHOM HE WOULD BE DEAD BY NOW!

THANKS ALSO TO THE GODS

THE GODS... YEAH FOR HIS LUCK HE SHOULD THANK THEM ALL BY CLOSING HIMSELF UP FOR A WEEK IN THE...

...PANTHEON

IT SURE IS ONE OF THE BIGGEST AND BEST KEPT MONUMENTS EVER BUILT; ITS NAME COMES FROM GREEK AND TELLS US THAT THE TEMPLE WAS DEDICATED TO ALL THE GODS!

DID YOU KNOW!? THE PANTHEON'S DOME IS THE PERFECT SECTION OF A GIGANTIC IMAGINARY SPHERE THAT COULD BE HELD INSIDE. IT WAS TO GIVE YOU THE IMPRESSION OF BEING INSIDE HEAVEN'S VAULT AND CLOSER TO THE GODS!

WHAT WE SEE TODAY IS THE LATEST VERSION OF THE PANTHEON, BUILT BY HADRIAN AROUND 118-125 AD; YEAH BECAUSE IN ROME MANY TIMES BUILDINGS WERE TORN DOWN TO MAKE PLACE FOR NEW ONES.. BUT HADRIAN PLAYED FAIR, HE PUT UP AN INSCRIPTION REMINDING THAT THE PREVIOUS FIRST TEMPLE HAD BEEN BUILT BY AGRIPPA IN 27 BC

THE DOME BEING SO HUGE, COULDN'T WEIGH TOO MUCH OTHERWISE...BLAM! THAT'S WHY THE CLEVER ROMAN ARCHITECTS FOUND VARIOUS WAYS TO MAKE IT LIGHT: THEY USED VEEERY LIGHTWEIGHT MATERIALS OF VOLCANIC ORIGIN AND DECORATED THE VAULT'S INNER SIDE WITH LARGE SQUARE HOLES, SUNKEN COFFERS, MADE WITH PYRAMID FORM MOULDS WHICH USING LESS MATERIAL FURTHER RELIEVING THE OVERALL WEIGHT!

THE TEMPLE'S PLAN

THE DOME'S DIAMETER IS 43,30 METERS: IMAGINE 1 METER LARGER THAN SAINT PETER'S DOME!

THE PANTHEON IS SO WELL PRESERVED BECAUSE IN 609 AD IT WAS TRANSFORMED INTO A CHURCH, S. MARY OF THE MARTYRS. IN SPITE OF THIS THE BRONZE TILES THAT COVERED THE DOME WERE STILL STOLEN!!

79

GLOSSARIUM

A

AMPHITHEATER

AN ELLIPTICAL SHAPED PUBLIC BUILDING WHERE GLADIATOR COMBAT, ANIMAL HUNTING AND MOCK NAVAL BATTLES (NAUMACHIAE) TOOK PLACE.
THE EVENTS WHERE SHOWN IN THE "ARENA". THE "CAVEA" WAS THE PART WHERE THE SPECTATORS SAT.

APOLLODORUS OF DAMASCUS

ONE OF THE FEW ANCIENT ROMAN ARCHITECTS WHOSE NAME HAS REACHED US. AS AN ARMY ENGINEER HE FOLLOWED EMPEROR TRAJAN DURING HIS CAMPAIGNS AGAINST THE DACIANS, AND AFTERWARDS HE DESIGNED AND BUILT IN ROME THE HUGE MONUMENTAL COMPLEX OF THE TRAJAN FORA AND MARKETS GIVING PROOF OF HIS INGENUITY AND CAPACITY OF FINDING NEW ARCHITECTURAL SOLUTIONS.
AFTER TRAJAN'S DEATH HE WAS AT EMPEROR HADRIAN'S SERVICE WHO, OFFENDED BY APOLLODORUS'S CRITICISMS TO HIS ARCHITECTURAL PROJECTS, EXILED HIM AND MAYBE HAD HIM EXECUTED.

APSE

SEMICIRCULAR STRUCTURE PLACED AT THE END OF THE CENTRAL NAVE IN ROMAN BASILICAE AND WHERE TRIALS WERE HELD.

B

BRUTUS (AND CASSIUS)
(MARCUS JUNIUS BRUTUS CAEPIO) 85 BC - 42 BC

SON OF A PLEBEIAN TRIBUNE AND OF SERVILIA COEPIONIS, WHO WAS JULIUS CAESAR'S MISTRESS, BECAME GOVERNOR OF GAUL AND THEN PRAETOR.
IN 44 B.C. OPPOSING THE DICTATORSHIP OF CAESAR, HE PARTICIPATED IN THE CONSPIRACY TO ASSASSINATE HIM WITH THE COMPLICITY OF HIS BROTHER IN LAW, CASSIUS, AND OTHER SENATORS. HE COMMITTED SUICIDE AFTER LOSING THE BATTLE OF PHILIPPI AGAINST MARC ANTONY AND AUGUSTUS.

AUGUSTUS
(CAIUS GIULIUS CAESAR OCTAVIAN AUGUSTUS) ROMAN EMPEROR FROM 27 BC TO 14 AD

HE WAS TO BECOME THE FIRST ROMAN EMPEROR BORN ON SEPTEMBER 23RD 63 BC HIS FATHER, FROM WHOM HE INHERITED HIS NAME ACCORDING TO ROMAN CUSTOM, DIED WHEN THE FUTURE AUGUSTUS WAS ONLY FOUR YEARS OLD: HE WAS BROUGHT UP BY HIS GRANDMOTHER, JULIA, SISTER TO JULIUS CAESAR WHO MADE HIM HIS HEIR. THIS FACT WAS MADE KNOWN AFTER THE DICTATOR'S ASSASSINATION.
OCTAVIUS WAS THEN 18: HE BECAME AN ALLY OF MARC ANTONY, AND DEFEATED CAESAR'S MURDER'S CHIEF CONSPIRATORS CASSIUS AND BRUTUS IN THE BATTLE OF PHILIPPI (OCTOBER 42 BC).
AFTER TEN YEARS OF A DIFFICULT RELATIONSHIP WITH ANTONY WHO HAD BEEN APPOINTED RULER OF THE ORIENTAL PROVINCES, HE FOUGHT AGAINST ANTONY AND CLEOPATRA AT THE NAVAL BATTLE OF ACTIUM, IN GREECE (31 BC). SUBSEQUENTLY ANTONY AND CLEOPATRA COMMITTED SUICIDE.
IN 27 BC THE ROMAN SENATE SOLEMNLY GRANTED OCTAVIAN THE TITLE OF IMPERATOR, NOT AS A NAME BUT AS A SURNAME WITH THE FACULTY OF PASSING IT DOWN TO HIS HEIRS, AND TO WHICH WAS ADDED THE NAME OF AUGUSTUS.

C

CAESAR
(CAIUS JULIUS CAESAR) 100 BC-44 BC

BORN FROM AN ANCIENT PATRICIAN FAMILY, THE GENS JULIA. HE COVERED VARIOUS POSITIONS IN THE REPUBLIC. IN 59 BC HE STROKE UP AN ALLIANCE WITH THE GENERAL POMPEUS, BECAME CONSUL AND OBTAINED VARIOUS PRESTIGIOUS APPOINTMENTS, SUCH AS GOVERNOR OF CISALPINE GAUL (PRESENT DAY LOMBARDY) AND OF NARBONESE GAUL (NOW PROVENCE, FRANCE). AFTER A CAMPAIGN LASTING 8 YEARS AGAINST THE GALLIC, BELGIAN AND GERMANIC TRIBES. HE SUBDUED THE REVOLT DEFEATING VERCINGETORIX AT ALESIA AND CONQUERING THE ENTIRE TERRITORY OF THE THREE GALLIA , (NOW FRANCE, BELGIUM, HOLLAND AND SWITZERLAND). HE WAS THE FIRST TO LEAD A FLEET ACROSS

THE ENGLISH CHANNEL FOR A PUNITIVE EXPEDITION AGAINST THE BRITANNIC TRIBES. IN THE MEANTIME POMPEUS AND HIS POLITICAL ENEMIES IN ROME WERE CONSPIRING AGAINST HIM, TRYING TO BLOCK HIS ACCESS TO POWER. IN 49 B.C. WHILE RETURNING FROM GALLIA AT THE HEAD OF THE STRONGEST OF ROMAN ARMIES HE LEAD HIS LEGIONS ACROSS THE RUBICON RIVER WHERE HE STATED THE FAMOUS PHRASE "ALEA IACTA EST" THE DIE IS CAST" AND OFFICIALLY STARTED A CIVIL WAR WHICH EVENTUALLY MADE HIM THE UNDISPUTED LEADER OF ROME: HE DEFEATED POMPEUS AT PHARSALUS IN 48 B.C. AFTER RETURNING TO ROME WITH THE EXTRAORDINARY POWERS OF DICTATOR, HE WAS ASSASSINATED ON THE IDES OF MARCH (MARCH 15TH) OF 44 B.C. VICTIM OF A CONSPIRACY.

CARACALLA (LUCIUS SEPTIMIUS BASSIANUS MARCUS AURELIUS ANTONINUS) ROMAN EMPEROR FROM 211 TO 217 AD

ELDER SON OF EMPEROR SEPTIMIUS SEVERUS, WAS BORN IN LUGDUNUM, GAUL (NOW LYON, FRANCE) ON APRIL 4TH 188 AD. HIS NICKNAME, CARACALLA, WAS AFTER A GALLIC HOODED TUNIC HE USUALLY WORE . AFTER HIS FATHER'S DEATH (211 AD) HE HAD HIS YOUNGER BROTHER, GETA, WHOM HE HATED AND WITH WHOM HE HAD INITIALLY RULED THE EMPIRE, MURDERED. IN SPITE OF HIS VIOLENT AND RUTHLESS CHARACTER, HE PROMULGATED MANY IMPORTANT ADMINISTRATIVE REFORMS AMONG WHICH A LAW GRANTING ROMAN CITIZENSHIP TO ALL FREEMEN THROUGHOUT THE EMPIRE. HE WAS MURDERED BY HIS SOLDIERS IN MESOPOTAMIA.

CLEOPATRA
(CLEOPATRA VII PHILOPATOR) 69 BC TO 30 BC

SHE WAS THE LAST AND MOST FAMOUS QUEEN OF EGYPT. HER LIFE BECAME A LEGEND AND WAS DRAMATIC: A STRONG AND DETERMINED WOMAN, SHE MADE USE OF JULIUS CAESAR'S PROTECTION FROM WHOM SHE HAD A SON, CAESARION, TO STABILIZE AND REINFORCE HER COUNTRY IN ITS RELATION WITH ROME. SHE LATER BECAME THE MISTRESS AND ALLY OF ANTONY, CONTROLLING WITH HIM THE EASTERN PART OF THE ROMAN EMPIRE. OCTAVIAN DECLARED WAR AGAINST HER AND DEFEATED, AT ACTIUM, THE EGYPTIAN FLEET LED BY ANTONY. CLEOPATRA COMMITTED SUICIDE BY INDUCING A POISONOUS SNAKE, AN ASP TO BITE HER.

COMMODUS
(LUCIUS AELIUS AURELIUS ANTONINUS COMMODUS)
ROMAN EMPEROR FROM 180 TO 192 AD

EMPEROR MARCUS AURELIUS'S SON. COMMODUS BECAME EMPEROR AT THE AGE OF 18. AND AS TOLD BY ANCIENT HISTORIANS HE WAS ONE OF THE WORST EMPERORS OF ROME: NOT CULTURED. BLOODTHIRSTY AND INDIFFERENT TO THE EMPIRE'S INTERESTS. HAVING A PASSION FOR GLADIATORIAL COMBAT HE COMPETED IN THE ARENA. HE DIED OF POISONING AT THE AGE OF 32. HIS CHARACTER WAS DESCRIBED IN THE FILM "THE GLADIATOR".

CONSTANTINE
(FLAVIUS VALERIUS CONSTANTINUS) ROMAN EMPEROR FROM 306 AD TO 337 AD

HE WAS ONE OF THE MOST IMPORTANT EMPERORS OF ROMAN HISTORY. HE ROSE TO POWER BY DEFEATING HIS RIVAL MAXENTIUS AFTER A LONG CIVIL WAR WHICH ENDED WITH THE BATTLE AT THE MILVIAN BRIDGE IN OCTOBER 312 AD THE SITE OF WHICH CAN STILL BE SEEN TODAY. HE WAS THE FIRST EMPEROR TO RECOGNIZE CHRISTIAN RELIGION AND TO ALLOW FREEDOM OF THE CULT WHICH UNTIL THEN HAD BEEN PERSECUTED. HE HIMSELF CONVERTED TO THE NEW RELIGION. FAVOURING THE CONSTRUCTION OF MANY CHURCHES AMONG WHICH THE ONE THAT BECAME SAINT PETER'S BASILICA. HE MOVED THE CAPITAL OF THE ROMAN EMPIRE TO BYZANTIUM.

D

DOMITIAN
(TITUS FLAVIUS DOMITIANUS) EMPEROR OF ROME FROM 81 AD TO 96 AD

YOUNGEST SON OF EMPEROR VESPASIANUS AND TITUS'S BROTHER. HE BECAME EMPEROR AT THE LATTER'S DEATH. VERY BAD ADMINISTRATOR. HE WAS KILLED BY A CONSPIRATION OF SENATORS.

E

ETRUSCANS
ANCIENT ITALIC PEOPLE THAT LIVED IN THE PRESENT DAY REGIONS OF UMBRIA. TUSCANY AND NORTHERN LATIUM (MAINLY CENTRAL ITALY) FROM THE VIII CENTURY BC. AFTER A LONG SERIES OF WARS THEY WERE CONQUERED BY ROME AND ASSIMILATED.

F

FASCES LICTORIAE
A BUNDLE OF BIRCH RODS TIED TOGETHER WITH A RED LEATHER RIBBON INTO A CYLINDER. OFTEN INCLUDING AN AXE AT THE END WITH THE BLADE PROJECTING FROM THE SIDE. THE RODS SYMBOLIZED PUNISHMENT. CULPRITS OR WHO WAS DISOBEDIENT WERE WHIPPED WITH THE RODS. THE LEATHER RIBBON SYMBOLISED UNION WHILE THE AXE POWER OF LIFE OR DEATH. THE FASCES LICTORIAE WERE CARRIED IN PARADES. IN FRONT OF THE STATESMEN. BY LICTORS DRESSED IN TOGAE WHO WERE ROMAN CITIZENS ASSIGNED TO PROTECT THE HIGH PUBLIC OFFICIALS. THE MORE THE FASCES LICTORIAE SHOWN THE HIGHER THE RANK OF THE OFFICIAL.

H

HADRIAN
(PUBLIUS AELIUS TRAJANUS ADRIANUS) ROMAN EMPEROR FROM 117 TO 138 AD

BORN IN SPAIN. AS HIS PREDECESSOR AND TUTOR TRAJAN WHO HAD ADOPTED HIM UPON HIS DEATH. HE WAS PROCLAIMED EMPEROR AT THE AGE OF 40.
CULTURED AND ILLUMINATED. HE WAS A SKILLFUL ORGANIZER OF THE EMPIRE. OF WHICH. LOVING TO TRAVEL. HE VISITED MANY PROVINCES: HE PREFERRED PEACE AND PROMOTED LARGE URBAN PROJECTS ALSO IN ROME AND ITS SURROUNDINGS. HADRIAN'S AGE WAS A PERIOD OF VERY INTENSE BUILDING ACTIVITY SUCH AS THE PANTHEON. THE TEMPLE OF VENUS AND ROME. HIS MAUSOLEUM: ONE OF HIS FOREMOST ARCHITECTURAL FEATS WAS HIS VILLA. A SPLENDID IMPERIAL RESIDENCE AT TIVOLI WHICH WAS FINISHED IN 134 AD HADRIAN DIED AT 62 AND APPOINTED AS HIS SUCCESSOR ANTONINUS PIUS.

L

LATINS
ANCIENT PRE-ROMAN ITALIC PEOPLE THAT LIVED FROM THE 8TH CENTURY BC. IN CENTRAL AND SOUTHERN LATIUM. FROM ONE OF THESE LATIN COMMUNITIES ROME WAS BORN.

M

MARCUS AURELIUS
(CAESAR MARCUS AURELIUS ANTONINUS AUGUSTUS)
ROMAN EMPEROR FROM 161 TO 180 AD

EMPEROR AND PHILOSOPHER. MARCUS AURELIUS HAD BEEN ADOPTED BY HIS UNCLE ANTONINUS PIUS WHO APPOINTED HIM AS HIS SUCCESSOR. HE WAS EMPEROR TOGETHER WITH HIS BROTHER LUCIUS VERUS UNTIL 168 AD. AND THEN BY HIMSELF FOR ANOTHER 11 YEARS. CONSIDERED AS A CULTIVATED AND ILLUMINATED PERSON BY ANCIENT HISTORIANS, HE WAS CONTRARY TO VIOLENCE AND PEACE WAS HIS UTMOST IDEAL OF HIS POLICY: HOWEVER HIS REIGN WAS UNFORTUNATELY MARKED BY WARS. FAMINE AND PLAGUES.
HE WAS PROMOTER OF IMPORTANT SOCIAL REFORMS SUCH AS EQUAL RIGHTS BETWEEN PATRICIANS AND PLEBEIANS. HE FORBID GLADIATORIAL GAMES CONSIDERING THEM TOO VIOLENT.

MAXENTIUS
(MARCUS AURELIUS VALERIUS MAXENTIUS) 278 TO 312 AD

SON OF MAXIMIAN HERCULEUS. COLLABORATOR AND GENERAL OF EMPEROR DIOCLETIAN. HE PROCLAIMED HIMSELF EMPEROR PROFITING FROM THE CONFUSION CAUSED BY THE ABDICATION OF DIOCLETIAN. HE FOUGHT FOR A LONG TIME AGAINTS CONSTANTINE. THE FINAL BATTLE TOOK PLACE AT THE MILVIAN BRIDGE IN ROME WHERE MAXENTIUS LOST HIS LIFE.

N

NERO
(NERO CLAUDIUS CAESAR AUGUSTUS GERMANICUS) ROMAN EMPEROR FROM 54 TO 68 AD

HE WAS BORN IN ANTIUM NEAR ROME FROM AGRIPPINA THE YOUNGER. GREAT-GRANDDAUGHTER OF AUGUSTUS.
HE WAS ADOPTED AND CHOSEN AS HEIR BY EMPEROR CLAUDIUS WHOM HE SUCCEEDED WHEN THE LATTER DIED MAYBE POISONED BY AGRIPPINA HERSELF WHO WANTED HER SON TO RISE TO POWER.
HISTORY TELLS HOW HE WAS AN INSANE. CRUEL EMPEROR WHO LIVED A LIFE OF VICE. HOWEVER HE ALSO PROMULGATED A MONETARY REFORM THAT WAS VERY IMPORTANT FOR THE EMPIRE'S HISTORY AND HAD HIMSELF BUILT IN ROME A SUMPTUOUS RESIDENCE. THE DOMUS AUREA.

NOMEN

THIS TERM INDICATES A GROUP OF PERSONS, GENS, WHO ALL HAD THE SAME FAMILY ORIGIN, OF THE SAME DYNASTY: I.E. DYNASTY OF THE FLAVIANS, OF THE ULPIANS, OF THE GIULII. NAMES IN ANCIENT ROME INCLUDED A PRAENOMEN (NAME), THEN THE NOMEN (FAMILY OR GENS TO WHICH ONE BELONGED) AND FINALLY THE COGNOMEN (NICKNAME) WHICH USUALLY INDICATED A CHARACTERISTIC OF THE PERSON (FAT, LAME, ETC.).

P

PLEBEIANS AND PATRICIANS

THE PLEBEIANS WERE ROMAN CITIZENS WHO DID NOT BELONG TO THE ANCIENT AND NOBLE ROMAN FAMILIES, THE PATRICIANS. THE PLEBEIANS WERE INITIALLY EXCLUDED FROM PUBLIC OFFICE. FROM 495 BC TO 454 BC THEY STARTED A SERIES OF REVOLTS TO ASSERT THEIR RIGHTS AS CITIZENS.
THE PEAK OF THE REVOLT WAS WHEN THE PLEBEIANS LEFT THE CITY AND OBLIGING THE PATRICIANS TO ACCEPT THE FIGURE OF A "TRIBUNE OF THE PLEBE" THAT IS A REPRESENTATIVE OF THE PEOPLE ENDOWED WITH IMMUNITY ENTITLED TO DISCUSS AND NEGOTIATE WITH THE CONSULS. THE REVOLTS OF THE PLEBE ENDED FOLLOWING THE DECISION TO MAKE EQUAL LAWS FOR BOTH PATRICIANS AND PLEBEIANS: THE "LAWS OF (FIRST THE 10 AND THEN THE) 12 TABLES".

PUNIC WARS

THE THREE WARS THAT ROME FOUGHT AND WON DURING THE REPUBLICAN ERA FROM 241 TO 147 BC AGAINTS THE CARTHAGINIANS WHO HAD A STRONG NAVY THAT DOMINATED THE MEDITERRANEAN SEA. THE ROMANS, WHEN THEY EXPANDED INTO SOUTHERN ITALY ENTERED INTO CONFLICT WITH SOME CARTHAGINIAN COLONIES IN SICILY FOR THE CONTROL OF THE SEA ROUTES AROUND ITALY. THE THREE WARS, DURING WHICH FIERCE FIELD BATTLES AND GREAT NAVAL ENCOUNTERS WERE FOUGHT ENDED WITH ROME'S VICTORIOUS DESTRUCTION OF THE CARTHAGINIAN CITY STATE, IN PRESENT DAY TUNISIA, CARTHAGE, IN 141 BC.

S

SABINES

ANCIENT ITALIC TRIBE INHABITING LATIUM AND SOUTHERN ABRUZZI BEFORE THE FOUNDING OF ROME. THEY WERE ASSIMILATED BY THE ROMANS IN THE IIIRD CENTURY BC.

SAMNITES

GROUP OF ANCIENT ITALIC TRIBES INHABITING A TERRITORY OF THE CENTRAL AND SOUTHERN APPENINES, THEN CALLED SAMNIUM , CORRESPONDING TO PRESENT DAY ABRUZZI, NORTHERN CAMPANIA, NORTHERN PUGLIA, MOLISE AND BASILICATA. BETWEEN THE IVTH AND IIIRD CENTURIES BC. THE SAMNITES AND THE ROMANS FOUGHT IN A SERIES OF WARS FOR THE CONTROL OF CENTRAL AND SOUTHERN ITALY WHICH WERE FINALLY WON BY THE ROMANS.

SEPTIMIUS SEVERUS
(LUCIUS SEPTIMIUS SEVERUS) ROMAN EMPEROR FROM 193 AD TO 211 AD

BORN IN LEPTIS IN NORTHERN AFRICA (TODAY'S LIBYA) ROSE TO POWER SUPPORTED BY HIS LEGIONS WHEN HE WAS GOVERNOR OF PANNONIA (THE REGION THAT INCLUDED PARTS OF PRESENT DAY HUNGARY, AUSTRIA, CROATIA AND SLOVENIA), DEFEATING HIS OPPONENTS. A COOL AND INTELLIGENT POLITICIAN DURING HIS RULE HE SUPPORTED AND FAVOURED THE MILITARY CLASS, AMONG OTHER, ALLOWING SOLDIERS TO LIVE WITH THEIR WIVES. HE HAD TWO SONS CARACALLA AND GETA.

SUBURRA

A TEEMING PROLETARIAN QUARTER OF ANCIENT ROME, THAT EXTENDED OVER THE QUIRINALE, THE VIMINALE AND THE ESQUILINO HILLS AND WHERE FIRES BROKE OUT FREQUENTLY.

T

TITUS
(TITUS FLAVIUS CEASAR) ROMAN EMPEROR FROM 79 TO 81 AD

ELDEST SON OF EMPEROR VESPASIAN. A CLEVER GENERAL HE CONCLUDED THE WAR IN JUDEA WITH THE SACKING AND DESTRUCTION OF THE GREAT TEMPLE IN JERUSALEM.

ONCE HE BECAME EMPEROR HE COMPLETED THE CONSTRUCTION OF THE COLOSSEUM AND INAUGURATED THE FIRS GAMES.

TRAJAN
(MARCUS ULPIUS NERVA TRAJAN) ROMAN EMPEROR FROM 98 TO 117 AD

BORN IN SPAIN FROM A SENATORIAL FAMILY, THE ULPI, HE WA A VERY ABLE GENERAL ALREADY UNDER EMPEROR DOMITIAN DURING THE GERMANIC WARS; HE WAS ADOPTED BY NERV AS HIS SUCCESSOR. IN 97 AD HE BECAME EMPEROR. THE FIRS NON ITALIAN EMPEROR ONE YEAR LATER AT AGE 45. HE WAS CLEVER AND PRUDENT STATESMAN AND WAS ABLE TO BE AC CEPTED BY THE SENATE. THE MIDDLE CLASS AND THE ARMY HE CONQUERED DACIA AFTER TWO MILITARY CAMPAIGN CELEBRATED ON THE TRAJAN COLUMN AND CREATED TH PROVINCE OF ARABIA. UNDER HIS RULE THE ROMAN EMPIR REACHED ITS GREATEST EXTENSION.

V

VESPASIAN
(TITUS FLAVIUS VESPASIANUS) ROMAN EMPEROR FROM 6 TO 79 AD

FIRST CONSUL THEN GOVERNOR OF AFRICA, HE COMANDE THE ROMAN ARMY IN THE JEWISH-ROMAN WARS.
HE WAS PROCLAIMED EMPEROR AFTER A CIVIL WAR FOLLOW ING THE DEATH OF EMPEROR NERO WHILE HIS TWO SON TITUS AND DOMITIAN, FUTURE ROMAN EMPERORS, WER ELECTED CONSULS.

VIRGIL
(PUBLIUS VIRGILIUS MARO) 70 TO 19 BC

LATIN POET. HE WAS BORN AT ANDES, NEAR PRESENT DA MANTUA, SON OF A LAND OWNER. HE STUDIED PHILOSOPH MEDICINE AND MATHEMATICS. HE WROTE IMPORTANT WORK LIKE THE BUCOLICS OR ECLOGUES AND THE GEORGICS.
HE BECAME A FAVOURITE OF AUGUST AND HIS EMPIRE'S OFFICIA POET. TO CELEBRATE THE JULIA DYNASTY OF AUGUSTUS, H WROTE THE AENEID, AN EPIC TELLING THE STORY OF TH MYTHICAL TROJAN PRINCE AENEAS'S VOYAGE FROM TROY T LATIUM.